NUTRITION AND DIET RESEARCH PROGRESS

WEIGHTY FACTORS IN CHILDREN'S FOOD AND BEVERAGE CONSUMPTION

Nutrition and Diet Research Progress

Additional books in this series can be found on Nova's website under the Series tab.

Additional E-books in this series can be found on Nova's website under the E-book tab.

Food and Beverage Consumption and Health

Additional books in this series can be found on Nova's website under the Series tab.

Additional E-books in this series can be found on Nova's website under the E-book tab.

NUTRITION AND DIET RESEARCH PROGRESS

WEIGHTY FACTORS IN CHILDREN'S FOOD AND BEVERAGE CONSUMPTION

CHARLES E. OYLER

AND

CHRISTINA DE VOLLD

EDITORS

nova publishers

New York

Copyright © 2013 by Nova Science Publishers, Inc.

For permission to use material from this book please contact us:
Telephone 631-231-7269; Fax 631-231-8175
Web Site: http://www.novapublishers.com

NOTICE TO THE READER

Additional color graphics may be available in the e-book version of this book.

Library of Congress Cataloging-in-Publication Data

ISBN: 978-1-62257-917-4

Published by Nova Science Publishers, Inc. † New York

CONTENTS

PREFACE

The prevalence of childhood obesity has risen dramatically in the last several decades in the United States, and is currently considered to be epidemic. This book examines the many factors that play a role in this crisis including the effect of food and beverage prices on children's weights; how food away from home affects children's diet quality; the environments to which children are exposed in their daily lives (ie., schools, child care, communities) can influence the healthfulness of their diets; and the potential effects on taxing caloric sweetened beverages.

Chapter 1 – One factor that may be important in explaining rising childhood obesity is food prices. This report explores the effect of food prices on children's Body Mass Index (BMI) using data from the Early Childhood Longitudinal Study, Kindergarten Class of 1998-99 (ECLS-K) and the Quarterly Food-at-Home Price Database.

On average, higher prices for soda, 100 percent juices, starchy vegetables, and sweet snacks are associated with lower BMIs among children. In addition, lower prices for dark green vegetables and lowfat milk are associated with reduced BMI. The effect of subsidizing healthy food may be just as large as raising prices of less healthy foods.

Chapter 2 – Based on two days of dietary data and panel data methods, this study includes estimates of how each child's consumption of food away from home, food from school (which includes all foods available for purchase at schools, not only those offered as part of USDA reimbursable meals), and caloric sweetened beverages affects that child's diet quality and calorie consumption. Compared with meals and snacks prepared at home, food prepared away from home increases caloric intake of children, especially older children. Each food-away-from-home meal adds 108 more calories to daily total intake among children ages 13-18 than a snack or meal from home; all food from school is estimated to add 145 more calories. Both food away from home and all food from school also lower the daily diet quality of older children (as measured by the 2005 Healthy Eating Index). Among younger children, who are more likely than older children to eat a USDA school meal and face a more healthful school food environment, the effect of food from school on caloric intake and diet quality does not differ significantly from that of food from home.

Chapter 3 – The current childhood obesity epidemic is the result of many factors and may not be resolved by any single action. Rather, resolution of the childhood obesity epidemic will require concerted action across many sectors and settings such as child care facilities, communities, and schools. The 2011 Children's Food Environment State Indicator Report highlights selected behaviors, environments, and policies that affect childhood obesity through support of healthy eating. These indicators represent opportunities for action.

Chapter 4 – The link between high U.S. obesity rates and the overconsumption of added sugars, largely from sodas and fruit drinks, has prompted public calls for a tax on caloric sweetened beverages. Faced with such a tax, consumers may reduce consumption of these sweetened beverages and substitute nontaxed beverages, such as bottled water, juice, and milk. This study estimated that a tax-induced 20-percent price increase on caloric sweetened beverages could cause an average reduction of 37 calories per day, or 3.8 pounds of body weight over a year, for adults and an average of 43 calories per day, or 4.5 pounds over a year, for children. Given these reductions in calorie consumption, results show an estimated decline in adult overweight prevalence (66.9 to 62.4 percent) and obesity prevalence (33.4 to 30.4 percent), as well as the child at-risk-for-overweight prevalence (32.3 to 27.0 percent) and the overweight prevalence (16.6 to 13.7 percent). Actual impacts would depend on many factors, including how the tax is reflected in consumer prices and the competitive strategies of beverage manufacturers and food retailers.

In: Weighty Factors in Children's Food…   ISBN: 978-1-62257-917-4
Editors: C.E. Oyler and C. De Volld   © 2013 Nova Science Publishers, Inc.

Chapter 1

THE EFFECT OF FOOD AND BEVERAGE PRICES ON CHILDREN'S WEIGHTS[*]

Minh Wendt and Jessica E. Todd

Photo credit: Shutterstock and Thinkstock.

---

[*] This is an edited, reformatted and augmented version of United States Department of Agriculture, Economic Research Report No. 118, dated June 2011.

ABSTRACT

One factor that may be important in explaining rising childhood obesity is food prices. This report explores the effect of food prices on children's Body Mass Index (BMI) using data from the Early Childhood Longitudinal Study, Kindergarten Class of 1998-99 (ECLS-K) and the Quarterly Food-at-Home Price Database.

On average, higher prices for soda, 100 percent juices, starchy vegetables, and sweet snacks are associated with lower BMIs among children. In addition, lower prices for dark green vegetables and lowfat milk are associated with reduced BMI. The effect of subsidizing healthy food may be just as large as raising prices of less healthy foods.

SUMMARY

The rate of overweight among children has tripled over the past 30 years. First Lady Michelle Obama's *Let's Move* campaign highlights the growing public interest in finding ways to reverse this trend. One factor that may be important in shaping children's dietary intake and weight is food prices. Previous research has shown that there is substantial geographic variation the relative price of healthy foods (Todd et al., 2011). This report estimates the effect of food prices on children's Body Mass Index (BMI) using variation in food prices across time and geographic areas.

WHAT DID THE STUDY FIND?

Food prices have small but statistically significant effects on children's BMI, but not all food prices have the same effect. While the magnitude of the price effects is similar for healthier and less healthy foods, the direction differs. Lower prices for some healthier foods, such as lowfat milk and dark green vegetables, are associated with decreases in children's BMI. In contrast, lower prices for soda, 100 percent juices, starchy vegetables, and sweet snacks are associated with increases in children's BMI.

These results show that the effect of subsidizing healthy food may be just as large as raising prices of less healthy foods. Specifically:

- A 10-percent price decrease for lowfat milk in the previous quarter is associated with a decrease in BMI of approximately 0.35 percent, or about 0.07 BMI units average for an 8- to 9-year-old.
- A 10-percent drop in the price of dark green vegetables (e.g., spinach and broccoli) in the previous quarter is associated with a reduction in BMI of 0.28 percent.
- A decrease in the price of sweet snacks during the previous quarter is associated with an increase in BMI of 0.27 percent.

Not surprisingly, there is sometimes a delay between when prices change and when measurable changes occur in children's BMI.

- A 10-percent price increase for carbonated beverages 1 year prior is associated with a decrease of 0.42 percent in the average child's BMI. The same price increase for 100 percent juices or starchy vegetables (e.g., potatoes and corn) is associated with a decrease in BMI of 0.3 percent 1 year later.

In addition to the effects varying over time, the effects of prices vary by other characteristics.

- Soda prices have a greater effect on children in households with income below 200 percent of the Federal poverty line, as compared with children in households with higher income.
- Prices for healthy foods such as lowfat milk and green vegetables have larger effects on higher BMI children than on children of average weight.
- Prices for less healthy food groups such as carbonated beverages, fruit drinks, and starchy vegetables have larger effects on BMI for children of average weight.

HOW WAS THE STUDY CONDUCTED?

Panel data on children's BMI, demographic, and household characteristics from the Early Childhood Longitudinal Study, Kindergarten Class of 1998-99 were linked to average retail food prices from the Quarterly Food-atHome Price Database. BMI was regressed on lagged prices (one-quarter and 1-year lags) using fixed-effects regressions to control for unobserved factors that are likely correlated with BMI. Alternative specifications included price changes over the previous quarter and previous year. Regressions were conducted on the full sample and also separately for boys and girls. Quantile regressions were used to explore whether heavier children have different responses to food prices than thinner children.

INTRODUCTION

The prevalence of childhood overweight has risen dramatically in the last several decades in the United States, and is currently considered to be epidemic (U.S. Department of Health and Human Services, 2007; Institute of Medicine, 2008). According to the Centers of Disease Control and Prevention (CDC), overweight rates of U.S. children and adolescents age 6-11 have more than tripled in the last 3 decades, from 6.5 percent in the 1970s to 19.6 percent in 2007-08 (Ogden and Carroll, 2010).[1] Moreover, the extent to which children's body mass index (BMI) exceeds the overweight threshold is also increasing (Flegal and Troiano, 2000; Jolliffe, 2004).

Childhood overweight is linked to a number of medical problems such as type II diabetes, high blood pressure, sleep apnea, and breathing problems; obese children are also more likely to become obese adults than are children of normal weight (U.S. DHHS, 2007; Steinberger et al., 2001; Must and Strauss, 1999; Whitaker et al., 1997). For children and adolescents age 6 to 17, overweight-related hospital costs increased more than threefold from $35 million per year during 1979-81 to $127 million during 1997-99 (Wang and Dietz, 2002).[2] As overweight and obese children become adults, their weight-related morbidities will lead to even greater economic costs. Medical costs of obesity in the United States were estimated to be as high as $147 billion in 2008, up from $78.5 billion in 1998 (Finkelstein et al., 2009).

First Lady Michelle Obama's *Let's Move* campaign highlights the growing national interest in identifying ways to reverse this trend. Recognizing that obesity is the result of many interrelated factors, the campaign encourages families, schools, and communities to improve dietary intake and increase energy expenditure among children.

One factor that may be important in shaping children's dietary intake is food prices. Previous research has show that there is substantial geographic variation in both the absolute price of foods (Todd and Leibtag, 2010) as well as the relative price of healthy foods (Todd et al., 2011). Economic literature on consumer behavior has shown that consumers change their purchases in response to prices changes. Previous research has shown that own-price elasticities (the percentage change in purchases of a good from a 1-percent change in its price) of foods and beverages are relatively large, ranging from 0.27 to 0.81, with food away from home, soft drinks, juice, and meat being most responsive to price changes (Andreyeva et al., 2010).

Recent studies have investigated the relationship between prices of certain food groups—such as meat, fruits/vegetables, and fast food—and childhood obesity. The consensus thus far is that higher prices for fast food and lower prices for fruits and vegetables are associated with lower children's weights (Auld and Powell, 2009; Powell and Bao, 2009; Sturm and Datar, 2008, 2005). However, while these studies examined the effect of market-level food prices, they did not study the effect of beverage prices.

This study's main innovation is to estimate the impact of food prices on childhood obesity by directly linking a unique database of food prices, the Quarterly Food-at-Home-Price Database (QFAHPD), with clinically measured body mass of children. The average retail prices for five beverage types, two types of vegetables, and sweet snack foods are linked to a longitudinal database tracking children's height and weight from kindergarten through eighth grade. The QFAHPD allows the comparison of food and beverage prices over time within and across geographic areas, enabling us to identify the effect of food prices on children's weight status.

We estimate models that test whether prices of carbonated beverages, fruit drinks, 100 percent juices, lowfat milk, whole and 2% milk, starchy vegetables (e.g., corn and potatoes), dark green vegetables (e.g., spinach and broccoli), and sweet snacks affect BMI among a cohort of U.S. children as they age from 5 to 14 years old. We selected these food groups because, with the exception of dark green vegetables, they represent a substantial portion of daily calorie intake among children and adolescents. Nielsen and Popkin (2004) show that soft drinks, fruit drinks, milk, fruit juice, and other beverages comprised 22.4 percent of daily calorie intake for children 2-18 years old in 1999-2001. Almost half of these beverage calories (10.3 percent) were from soft drinks and fruit drinks. Reedy and Krebs-Smith (2010) show that grain-based desserts (e.g., cakes and cookies) comprised 7.2 percent of average daily caloric intake among children age 2-18 in 2005-06. We include prices for dark green vegetables because they are nutrient-dense and low-calorie alternatives to starchy vegetables.

FOOD AND BEVERAGE PRICES AND CONSUMPTION AMONG U.S. CHILDREN AND ADOLESCENTS

The price index for carbonated drinks has been below both the consumer price index (CPI) and the indexes for all non-alcoholic beverages and whole milk over the last 25 years or so (fig. 1). That is, the real prices for carbonated drinks are actually declining over time. In contrast, the price index for all fruits and vegetables,[3] particularly fresh, is increasing faster than the CPI.[4]

At the same time, consumption of carbonated sweetened beverages (CSBs) and fruit drinks has increased among U.S. children and adolescents, while consumption of milk has declined. Mean intake of CSBs more than doubled, from 5 fluid ounces per day in 1977-78 to 12 fluid ounces in 1994-98 (fig. 2). Per capita daily caloric contribution from CSBs and 100 percent fruit juices increased from 242 kcal per day in 1988-94 to 270 kcal per day in 1999-2004. The largest increase—of about 20 percent—occurred among children age 6 to 11 years (Wang et al., 2008).

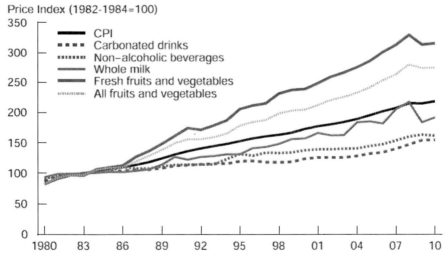

Notes: Prices for each group are annual average prices for all urban consumers. All fruits and vegetables include fresh, canned, and frozen. Base period 1982-84=100.

Source: Bureau of Labor Statistics, http://data.bls.gov/pdq/querytool.jsp?survey=cu.

Figure 1. Price indexes for selected foods and beverages, 1980-2010.

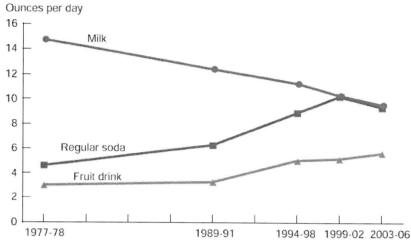

Source: Smith et al., 2010. Data are from 1977-78, NFCS (Nationwide Food Consumption Survey), USDA; 1989-91 and 1994-98 CSFII (Continuing Survey of Food Intakes by Individuals), USDA; 1999-2006 NHANES (National Health and Nutrition Examination Survey).

Figure 2. Soda, fruit drink, and milk consumption trend for children age 2-19, 1977-78 to 2003-06.

The combination of lower real prices and increased consumption lead many to argue that prices have a strong influence on consumption. However, this is ultimately an empirical question, as the full price effect depends on how much intake responds to price and how much weight changes in response to changes in caloric intake (Chow and Hall, 2008). We estimate the (reduced form) relationship between price and weight outcomes based on a traditional household economic framework.

APPLYING THE HOUSEHOLD ECONOMIC FRAMEWORK

The household production function (Becker, 1965) has been widely used in economics to study determinants of children's health in the United States (Variyam et al., 1999; Senauer and Garcia, 1991). In this framework, households combine time, human capital (knowledge and skills), and purchased goods to produce outcomes—such as health of a child—to maximize the overall household's utility. The market goods purchased by households (e.g., foods) derive their values by supplying characteristics (e.g., nutrients) necessary for the production of the outcome (e.g., body weight), in addition to other benefits such as taste and socialization while eating. In this model, when the price of a particular type of food increases, households reduce their consumption of that food in order to equate price with the benefit enjoyed from the last unit purchased (marginal utility).[5] Since weight is determined by net energy intake, we assume that children's body weight is determined by food intake as well as other factors (X) that would affect activity, such as household income and parents' education.

$$BMI = f(food, X) \tag{1}$$

Food intake is, in turn, determined by food prices, income, and demographic factors that affect preferences (Z).

$$Food = g(food\ prices, income, Z) \tag{2}$$

Since we do not directly observe the amount of food consumed by individuals, we can substitute equation 2 into equation 1 and obtain a (reduced-form) equation for children's BMI.

$$BMI = k(food\ prices, income, Z, X) \tag{3}$$

Thus, we can think of a child's weight or BMI as determined by food prices, income, and other factors, such as personal characteristics. Equation 3 allows us to estimate the effect of food prices on BMI, recognizing that the effect is transmitted through the effect that prices have on food intake.

DATA AND VARIABLES

Individual and Household Data

Individual and household data are from the Early Childhood Longitudinal Study, Kindergarten Class of 1998-99 (ECLS-K). The ECLS-K is a nationally representative sample of kindergarten students who were in kindergarten during the 1998-99 school year. Children are observed in kindergarten as well as during 1st, 3rd, 5th, and 8th grade. The five rounds of data used in this study correspond to the 1998-99, 1999-2000, 2001-02, 2003-04, and 2006-07 school years.[6]

The ECLS-K includes detailed household information, students' demo-graphics, parents' background and characteristics, as well as classroom and school environment. An advantage of this survey is that, unlike other child-level data that rely on self-reported measurements, children's height and weight were measured by survey staff and collected during all survey rounds. Some children are lost from the sample mainly because they changed schools or their families moved outside of the survey's primary sampling units. Approximately 50 percent of "movers" were randomly selected to be followed by ECLS-K. Therefore, most of the children lost for followup were those randomly selected and would be unlikely to bias the results. For more details on sample attrition, including nonresponse and change in eligibility status over time, see Tourangeau et al. (2009).

Food Price Data

Food prices are from the ERS Quarterly Food–at–Home Price Database (QFAHPD).[7] The QFAHPD was constructed from Nielsen Homescan data, in which households report their food-at-home purchases from all store types, including grocery stores, convenience stores, mass merchandisers, club stores, and supercenters. Average quarterly prices are provided for 52 narrowly defined food groups, such as carbonated soda, fruit drinks, and vegetables grouped by type (dark green, starchy, orange) and processing method (fresh, frozen, or canned). These prices were estimated as the weighted average of household-level quarterly prices for each food group, where the household-level prices are the mean price paid by each household for foods within each food group weighted by purchase frequency, not expenditure share within the food group (see Todd et al., 2010, for more details on the construction of the QFAHPD).

The QFAHPD includes prices for market areas covering the contiguous United States. There are 26 metropolitan markets, which are either single metro areas—such as Philadelphia, Baltimore, and Los Angeles—or a group of metro areas, such as Metro Ohio, which includes Cincinnati, Cleveland, and Columbus. Between 1998 and 2001, areas in the lower 48 States not included in these 26 metro markets are grouped into 4 nonmetro regions; between 2002 and 2006, they are grouped into 9 census divisions (see fig. A1). Although these prices are constructed from household-level purchase data, and therefore are affected by market-level demand, they allow for identification of price effects because they are averages for large geographic areas. This means that they are not sensitive to any one household's demand and are thus not influenced by individual household preferences.

The QFAHPD provides a list of all of the county Federal information processing standards (FIPS) codes covered by each market. We first assign a QFAHPD market to each child based on the child's county of residence and then merge the QFAHPD prices to each child-year observation. Since Alaska and Hawaii are not included in the QFAHPD (or in the Homescan data), 190 children living in these States in the ECLS-K sample are excluded from the analysis.[8] An additional 60 children from the lower 48 States are excluded because their FIPS county code lacks a corresponding code in the QFAHPD data (perhaps due to coding errors in ECLS-K or unidentified changes in FIPS coding over time). QFAHPD prices are nominal, so we convert them to real prices (in 2000 dollars) using the average monthly CPI for each quarter, calculated from monthly data from the Bureau of Labor Statistics.

Variables

Our main outcome variable is children's BMI as calculated from each child's survey-collected height and weight. Although each student's height and weight were measured by trained field workers, recording errors might occur. We check for consistency across survey waves to correct recording errors, and limit the range of extreme BMI measures using CDC growth charts. The 3rd percentile of BMI for children age 4 to 16 is 13.6, and the 97th percentile is 29.3 (CDC, 2000), so we limit the lowest BMI measure to 10 (affecting 50 children's measures) and the highest to 42 (affecting 90 children). We delete from the sample 10 children with obvious recording errors, such as having BMI greater than or equal to 98. We also determine whether each child is above the 85th (overweight) or 95th percentile (obese) of the growth charts in each wave using the assessment date information and children's birthdays (available in the restricted-use data) to calculate each child's age in months at the time height and weight were measured.[9]

To control for students' demographics and characteristics, we include their age, race, gender, and birth weight. Students' family structure is captured by their living arrangements categorized as living with two biological parents, one biological and one other parent, single mother, single father, or with adoptive parents or a guardian. We also control for household income relative to the poverty threshold (four categories) and parent's education level (five categories).

To control for market demand conditions, we include the median household income in the county for the year (obtained from the U.S. Census Bureau). To control for the overall price level of food, we include the average weekly price of a market basket (the Thrifty Food Plan, TFP) that provides a healthy diet to a family of four, constructed from the QFAHPD data, in real 2000 dollars. The TFP outlines the quantities (in pounds) of various food groups for individuals by age and gender that will provide a diet that meets the 2005 *Dietary Guidelines* at a low cost (Carlson et al., 2007). We use average market prices, not lowest cost, to construct the TFP basket cost for a family of four, so the measure reflects the average cost of a healthy diet in the child's market area (see Appendix B for more details on the construction of the TFP basket price).

Sample

Our analysis sample is limited to those students with nonmissing explanatory variables, for a total of 15,090 children, with 51,160 child-by-year observations. All children that live in Hawaii are excluded due to lack of food price information.[10]

The average BMI in the sample is 18.46, and obesity (BMI>95th percentile) is estimated at 16.2 percent (table 1). The obesity rate in our sample is comparable to national estimates for children age 6-11 (16.3 percent) and adolescents age 12-19 (16.7 percent) in 2001-02 from the National Health and Nutrition Examination Survey (Ogden and Carroll, 2010). The average age over all child-by-year observations is 106 months (a few months shy of 9 years old); 51 percent are girls, 64 percent are White, 5 percent are Asian, 11 percent are Black, 16 percent are Hispanic, and 4 percent are some other race or ethnicity.

Thirty-eight percent of the child-by-years have at least one parent who completed a college degree or more education, 34 percent have a parent whose highest education is some college, 21 percent have parents whose highest education is a high school degree, and 7 percent have parents with less than a high school education. About 68 percent of the sample lives with two biological parents. The other children in the sample live with two adults where one is a biological parent (9 percent), their single mother (19 percent), their single father (2 percent), or adoptive or foster parents (3 percent).

Table 1. Descriptive statistics
(N=51,160 observations on 15,090 children)

Variable	Mean	SD	Min	Max
Body Mass Index (BMI) - mean	18.46	4.18	10	42
Percent obese (BMI>95th percentile)	16.16			
Child characteristics				
Age (months)	105.64	32.85	52.50	190.50
Female	0.51	0.50	0	1
Birth weight (ounces)	118.57	21.10	16	219
White	0.64	0.48		
Asian	0.05	0.22		
Black	0.11	0.32		
Hispanic	0.16	0.36		
Other race/ethnicity	0.04	0.21		
Household/community characteristics Parents have less than high school education	0.07	0.26		
Parents completed high school	0.21	0.41		
Parents completed some college	0.34	0.47		
Parents completed college or more	0.38	0.48		
Household income >200% poverty threshold	0.64	0.48		
Household income between 130 and 200% poverty threshold	0.13	0.34		
Household income between 100 and 130% poverty threshold	0.07	0.26		
Household income below poverty threshold	0.16	0.36		
Child lives with 2 biological parents	0.68	0.47		
Child lives with 2 other parents	0.09	0.29		
Child lives with single mother	0.18	0.39		
Child lives with single father	0.02	0.13		
Child lives with other guardians	0.03	0.16		
County median annual household income ($)	44,870	11,758	17,344	104,984
(Prices, 1 quarter lag, $ per 100 grams) Carbonated beverages	0.07	0.01	0.06	0.09
Fruit drinks	0.11	0.02	0.07	0.19
100 percent juices	0.16	0.03	0.11	0.25
Lowfat milk (skim, and 1%)	0.09	0.01	0.05	0.12
Whole milk	0.11	0.01	0.08	0.14
Fresh and frozen dark green vegetables	0.26	0.03	0.19	0.41
Fresh and frozen starchy vegetables	0.17	0.02	0.11	0.24
Sweet snacks	0.74	0.07	0.60	1.07
Thrifty food plan basket weekly cost ($2000)	166.31	14.75	137.13	211.67

Note: Number of observation is rounded to the nearest 10.

Source: ERS calculations based on data from the Early Childhood Longitudinal Study, Kindergarten Class of 1998-99, rounds covering 1998-2007.

Mean QFAHPD prices across the sample (table 1) indicate that sweet snacks are the most expensive items per 100 grams (at $0.74), while carbonated beverages are the least expensive ($0.07). Lowfat milk is less expensive than whole milk ($0.09 vs. $0.11 per 100 grams); 100% juice ($0.16 per 100 grams) is more expensive than fruit drinks ($0.11) and carbonated beverages. Dark green vegetables are more expensive per 100 grams ($0.26) than starchy vegetables ($0.17). The average weekly TFP cost for a family of four was $166 over 1998-2007.

EMPIRICAL ANALYSIS

One of the most common concerns when estimating the effect of various factors on BMI is omitted variable bias, or failing to control for factors that might affect both the explanatory variable of interest (i.e. food prices) and the outcome (i.e., children's body weight). Examples of possible omitted variables in this study include availability of food retailers in an area and other neighborhood or locality characteristics. Since these factors are either unobservable or unavailable, econometric techniques should be used to reduce possible bias in the results. We employ the fixed-effects regression method, which controls for unobserved characteristics of each child—gender, race, and preferences for health and nutrition in the household—that do not change over time. We compare results from the fixed-effects model to a model that does not control for individual-level unobserved characteristics (ordinary least squares, OLS) to explore the extent to which ignoring these characteristics would change our estimated effects.[11] We also employ another model (quantile regression) to investigate whether the effects of prices differ for heavier versus thinner children (at different levels of the conditional BMI distribution).

More technically, since we are using a fixed-effects model (a within estimator), only the variation over time in BMI for each child is used to identify the effect of price. This gives us short-term estimates of the effects of price changes. In contrast, a cross-sectional model that uses only variation across geographic areas (across individuals) provides a longrun estimate of the effect of price. Thus, our contribution complements previous research by providing shortrun estimates of price effects. Given the frequency of food price spikes in recent years, the significance of shortrun price changes is heightened.

In our fixed-effects model, we compare results using different measures of price: the previous quarter's price and the price four quarters prior. Recent research indicates that changes in caloric intake take time to lead to changes in weight and vary according to the type of macronutrients consumed (Chow and Hall, 2008).[12] Comparing the results using the previous quarter's price to price from four quarters prior tests whether there are differences in when price changes result in weight changes. Given that the market definitions in QFAHPD change for "nonmetro" counties over the time period of the study, price changes in these areas may be due more to the changing definition of markets than actual price changes. Thus, we also estimate a model where children in these "nonmetro" areas are excluded to test the robustness of our full-sample results.

In our fixed-effects model, we include all child and household-level variables that vary over time, and in our OLS and quantile models, we include all child and household-level characteristics listed in table 1. In all models, we correct for clustering at the school level and for heteroscedasticity using the Huber-White covariance matrix.[13]

RESULTS

Average Effects of Food Prices

Table 2 reports the results from the fixed-effects (FE) and OLS models, providing estimates of the average associations between prices of selected foods/beverages and children's BMI. Generally, higher prices for lowfat milk and dark green vegetables are associated with higher body weight while higher prices for sweet snacks are correlated with lower weight 3 months later. On the other hand, when 1-year lagged prices are used, higher prices for carbonated beverages, 100 percent fruit juice, and starchy vegetables are associated with lower weight. This means that the effects of prices on body weight vary not only by type of food/drink, but that the same food or drink can have price effects that become more pronounced over time. The FE and OLS estimates differ, indicating that not accounting for unobserved characteristics would bias our estimates. Thus, our preferred model is FE, so we focus on interpreting the FE results going forward.

Since BMI and all prices are in log scale, the estimated coefficients tell us the percentage change in BMI associated with a 1-percent change in price. More technically, the estimated coefficients are the price elasticities of BMI. Unlike adults, children growing normally should see increases in BMI as they age. To provide context for the magnitude of the changes in BMI that are associated with price, we convert the percent changes to BMI unit changes using the average BMI in the sample. The BMI unit changes are actually quite small, but by comparing them to the expected change (growth) over 1 year at a certain point in the BMI distribution (such as the overweight threshold for a given age), we highlight the extent to which price influences short-term changes in BMI among children.

All else equal, a 10-percent price increase for lowfat milk in the previous quarter is associated with a 0.35-percent increase in children's BMI. For the average BMI measure in our sample, 18.5, at the average age of 8 years old (see table 1), such a price increase in lowfat milk equals an average increase of 0.07 unit of BMI. This is equivalent to about 13 percent of annual BMI growth for an 85th percentile boy, and 11 percent for an 85th percentile girl. This estimate assumes that a boy at the 85th percentile for BMI will gain about 0.5 BMI units between age 8 and 9 (2.8 percent, from 18.06 to 18.57), while a girl will gain 0.6 units (3.3 percent, from 18.44 to 19.06).

We also find that higher prices for dark green vegetables in the previous quarter are associated with greater BMI; a 10-percent price increase leads to an increase in BMI of 0.28 percent (or 0.05 unit, on average), equivalent to 10 percent and 8 percent of annual growth for a boy and girl, respectively, at the 85th percentile of BMI. The previous quarter's price of starchy vegetables is not significantly related to BMI.

On the other hand, a price increase for sweet snacks has an effect in magnitude similar to dark green vegetables, but with the opposite effect: a 10-percent increase is associated with a 0.27- percent decrease in BMI. Higher overall food prices, as measured by weekly cost of the TFP, reduce BMI, but including this variable does not affect our estimates for specific foods.

Results are different when we model 1-year lagged prices instead of the previous quarter's prices (column 2). A 10-percent price increase for carbonated beverages is associated with a decrease in BMI of 0.42 percent (0.08 unit) 1 year later, while a 10-percent price increase for 100 percent juices reduces BMI 0.3 percent (0.06 unit). A 10-percent price increase for fresh and frozen starchy vegetables is associated with a 0.3-percent decrease in BMI 1 year later. The 1-year lagged prices for carbonated beverages, 100 percent juices, and starchy vegetables are larger and statistically stronger than their one-quarter lagged prices, while the opposite is true for lowfat milk, dark green vegetables, and sweet snacks. This means that the prices of lowfat milk, dark green vegetables, and sweet snacks might have stronger immediate effects on children's BMI, while carbonated beverages, 100 percent juices, and starchy vegetables might either take some time to appear or have longlasting effects that get stronger over time.

Minh Wendt and Jessica E. Todd

Table 2. Estimation results, fixed-effects (FE) and OLS models, lagged prices

	FE			OLS	
	1st quarter	1-year	1-year1	1st quarter	1-year
BMI (Body Mass Index)	(1)	(2)	(3)	(4)	(5)
Carbonated beverages	-0.003	-0.042***	-0.030**	-0.028	-0.030
	(0.014)	(0.013)	(0.015)	(0.019)	(0.019)
Fruit drinks	0.004	-0.007	-0.013	-0.007	0.002
	(0.007)	(0.006)	(0.008)	(0.011)	(0.009)
100 percent juices	-0.005	-0.030***	-0.039***	-0.012	-0.030***
	(0.007)	(0.009)	(0.013)	(0.009)	(0.011)
Lowfat milk (skim, and 1%)	0.035***	0.012	0.011	0.019	0.036**
	(0.010)	(0.010)	(0.012)	(0.014)	(0.016)
Whole milk	0.001	0.008	0.006	-0.008	-0.022
	(0.007)	(0.010)	(0.011)	(0.012)	(0.017)
Fresh and frozen dark green vegetables	0.028**	0.012	0.024**	0.037*	0.047***
	(0.012)	(0.010)	(0.012)	(0.020)	(0.015)
Fresh and frozen starchy vegetables	-0.006	-0.030***	-0.013	-0.029**	-0.025*
	(0.008)	(0.007)	(0.008)	(0.014)	(0.013)
Sweet snacks	-0.027***	0.003	0.000	-0.008	0.000
	(0.008)	(0.010)	(0.011)	(0.015)	(0.016)
Thrifty Food Plan basket	-0.055**	-0.010	-0.058*	0.032	-0.025
	(0.027)	(0.026)	(0.032)	(0.045)	(0.034)
Number of observations	51,160	51,160	36,770	51,160	51,160
Number of student clusters	15,090	15,090	11,150		
R-squared (within)	0.710	0.710	0.699		
R-squared (between)	0.131	0.131	0.130		
R-squared (overall)	0.290	0.291	0.284	0.327	0.327

*** p < 0.01, ** p < 0.05, * p < 0.1.

Notes: Number of observations is rounded to the nearest 10. Standard errors in parentheses are adjusted using Huber-White covariance matrix estimate. FE control variables include the child's age (in months), household income, parent types, and survey round of data. The OLS control variables also include birth weight, indicators for whether the child is female, Asian, Black, Hispanic, or other race/ethnicity, and parent's education. BMI and all prices are in log scale.

[1] Children in the "nonmetro" areas in QFAHPD are excluded.

Source: ERS estimates using data from the Early Childhood Longitudinal Study, Kindergarten Class of 1998-99 and the Quarterly Food-atHome Price Database.

Approximately 25 percent of our sample resides in "nonmetro" areas as defined in the QFAHPD, and the definition of these areas changes slightly over the study's time period. Thus, the QFAHPD prices may not be as reliable for children in these areas as in the metro market areas. As a robustness check, we estimate the model using 4th quarter lag prices when these children are excluded. The results are fairly similar to those from the full sample, except for vegetables, in which the effect of the price of dark green vegetables is now positive and significant, while that for starchy vegetables is no longer significant (table 2, column 3).

Robustness Checks

Our results do not change when we use other measures of BMI and weight status, lending confidence to our main findings. Specifically, we test the sensitivity of our regression results in several ways.

First, we use standardized z-scores for BMI according to the U.S. 2000 reference growth charts as our dependent variable. Standardized z-scores compare the difference in an individual's BMI and the mean BMI in units of standard deviation.

Although we do control for age and gender in all of our models, standardized z-scores might be more sensitive to subtle changes in BMI for children across time. Second, we also use percentiles that are normalized from the BMI z-scores as a dependent variable.

While the percentiles are easier to match up with standard growth charts, they are bounded between 0 and 100, which poses some econometric challenges in selecting appropriate models for analyzing the data. Therefore, we use these results for confirming and validating purposes only. The results of these two alternative measures for BMI, although different in magnitude, are consistent in terms of signs and significance levels with our main model's results.[14]

Differences in Effects by BMI

It is possible that individuals of different BMIs might respond differently to changes in food prices. More precisely, do food prices affect children with higher BMI differently than children with lower BMI?

To test for this, we use quantile regression, an econometric method that allows us to compare the effects of prices across different levels of BMI.

Prices of healthier foods (e.g., lowfat milk, 100 percent juice, and dark green vegetables) have larger effects on children with higher BMI, while prices of less healthy foods (carbonated beverages, fruit drinks, whole milk, starchy vegetables) have greater impacts on children with lower BMI (table 3). One possible explanation for this is that while carbonated beverages are widely regarded as unhealthy drinks, less attention is devoted to other calorie-dense drinks such as fruit juice.

Therefore, parents might restrict overweight children from consuming soda but not other calorie-dense beverages. Another possibility is that preferences for carbonated beverages are more entrenched among heavier children, such that their consumption responds less to price as compared to children with lower BMI.

More technically, we use quantile regressions to test for heterogeneity in price responses examining the 25th, 50th, and 85th quantiles, estimating the effect of one-quarter and 1-year lagged prices separately.[15] It is difficult to incorporate individual fixed-effects in a quantile regression, but we are more interested in the pattern of response across the distribution of BMI and so we focus on comparing the results and not on individual coefficients per se.

Some interesting patterns emerge across the conditional distribution of BMI. First, for carbonated beverages, the effects of price are largest at the low end of the distribution and insignificant at the 85th quantile for both 1 quarter and 1-year lagged prices; the result is similar for starchy vegetables. In contrast, the effect of the price of 100 percent juices is largest at the 85th quantile (BMI), with a similar result for lowfat milk and dark green vegetables. The effects of prices for fruit drinks, 100 percent fruit juice, both types of milk, and dark green vegetables on the BMIs of children at the 85th quantile are statistically different from those for children at the median.

Our quantile regression results are similar to those of Auld and Powell (2009), although different specifications make it difficult to compare.

First, the price index used in Auld and Powell's study is for a group of seven fruits and vegetables, while ours has specific categories.

Second, they analyze a sample of adolescents while our sample is younger. Third, they include a price index for fast food but not for drinks, while we have specific categories for different drinks but not for fast food.

However, the overall conclusions are similar in that the price effects of certain foods are more significant for children at the 85th percentile compared to children at the median of the weight distribution.

Table 3. Estimation results, quantile regression, lagged prices

BMI (Body Mass Index)		Lagged prices				Lagged prices	
		1 quarter				1 year	
	25th quantile	50th quantile	85th quantile	25th quantile	50th quantile	85th quantile
	(1)	(2)	(3)	(4)	(5)	(6)
Carbonated beverages	-0.044***	-0.036**	-0.010	-0.032***	-0.026**	-0.000
	(0.013)	(0.014)	(0.024)	(0.011)	(0.012)	(0.026)
Fruit drinks	0.005	0.007	-0.019	0.017***	0.012*	-0.015
	(0.006)	(0.008)	(0.017)	(0.006)	(0.007)	(0.014)
100 percent juices	0.001	-0.012	-0.033**	-0.015**	-0.036***	-0.068***
	(0.007)	(0.007)	(0.015)	(0.006)	(0.007)	(0.018)
Lowfat milk (skim, and 1%)	0.003	0.014	0.048***	0.022**	0.026**	0.048**
	(0.008)	(0.009)	(0.018)	(0.009)	(0.011)	(0.023)
Whole milk	0.017**	-0.009	-0.034**	-0.012	-0.024**	-0.019
	(0.007)	(0.009)	(0.016)	(0.009)	(0.012)	(0.023)
Fresh and frozen dark green vegetables	0.006	0.041***	0.075***	0.019*	0.037***	0.082***
	(0.011)	(0.014)	(0.026)	(0.011)	(0.013)	(0.025)
Fresh and frozen starchy vegetables	-0.019*	-0.019	-0.025	-0.041***	-0.021**	0.007
	(0.010)	(0.013)	(0.018)	(0.009)	(0.010)	(0.023)
Sweet snacks	-0.012	-0.005	-0.021	-0.008	0.002	0.003
	(0.009)	(0.012)	(0.024)	(0.010)	(0.014)	(0.025)
Thrifty food plan basket	0.016	0.016	0.052	0.003	-0.004	-0.041
	(0.027)	(0.037)	(0.063)	(0.023)	(0.027)	(0.054)
Number of observations	51,380	51,380	51,380	51,380	51,380	51,380
Number of student clusters	15,090	15,090	15,090	15,090	15,090	15,090
Pseudo R-squared	0.151	0.192	0.228	0.151	0.193	0.228

*** $p < 0.01$, ** $p < 0.05$, * $p < 0.1$

Notes: Number of observations is rounded to the nearest 10. Tests of equality of the coefficients across the two quantiles for drinks (carbonated beverages, fruit drink, 100 percent juice, both types of milk) and foods (dark green vegetables, starchy vegetables, and sweet snacks) are statistically significant at 95%. Standard errors in parentheses are adjusted using Huber-White covariance matrix estimate. Fixed-effects control variables include the child's age (in months), household income, parent types, and survey round of data. The ordinary least squares control variables also include birth weight; indicators for whether the child is female, Asian, Black, Hispanic, or other race/ ethnicity; and parent's education. Body Mass Index and all prices are in log scale.

Source: ERS estimates using data from the Early Childhood Longitudinal Study, Kindergarten Class of 1998-99 and the Quarterly Food-atHome Price Database.

Subgroup Analyses

In addition to comparing effects by BMI, we estimate models for various population subgroups: gender, three income groups, and race (table 4). Overall, the effects of prices on children's body weight vary somewhat between boys and girls, across income levels, and among ethnic groups. Generally, girls' and boys' BMI responds similarly to food prices. The two exceptions are that a higher price for carbonated soda reduces boys' BMI but does not affect girls', while higher prices of dark green vegetables increases girls' BMI but not boys'. We also estimate separate models for three income groups: household income over 185 percent of the poverty line, between 130 and 185 percent of the poverty line, and at or below 130 percent of the poverty line. Consistent with expectations that price elasticities are smaller among higher income households, we find that higher prices of carbonated soda reduce BMI of children in households with income below 200 percent of the Federal poverty line, but not of children in higher income households. There is also variation across income groups in the significance of the prices of other foods (juice, dark green vegetables, and starchy vegetables).

Across racial groups, higher prices of carbonated beverages reduce BMI for White and Hispanic children, but not Blacks. Higher prices for juice reduce BMI of White and Black children, but not Hispanics. The price of starchy vegetables is significant for White children only.

IMPLICATIONS

There are three main implications of our findings. First, they support the idea that food prices have small, but statistically significant effects on children's BMI. Lower prices for soda, starchy vegetables, and sweet snacks have likely led to increases in children's BMI. The reverse is true for some healthier foods such as lowfat milk and dark green vegetables. Others have found that lower real prices for fruits and vegetables predict lower weight (Powell and Bao, 2009; Auld and Powell, 2009) or a smaller gain in BMI for young school-age children (Sturm and Datar, 2005, 2008). By separating the price of dark green vegetables from higher calorie starchy vegetables, we find that the price effect is not the same for all vegetables. A second implication of our analysis is that there may be a considerable delay between when prices change and measurable changes in children's BMI. That is, although changes in food prices might affect purchasing behavior immediately, effects on BMI are likely to take some time to appear, depending on the type of food. This finding highlights the need to have longitudinal data, allowing for individuals to be tracked over time and a rigorous examination of the longrun effects of changes in food prices on children's BMI and overweight status.

Third, these results highlight the fact that there are heterogeneous responses to changes in price, particularly across household income and the distribution of BMI. Larger effects among children in lower income households are consistent with economic theory that higher income households are less responsive to price. The finding of differences across the BMI distribution is consistent with Sturm et al. (2010), who found no average effect of State-level soda sales taxes on BMI, but a negative and statistically significant effect on BMI among children at or above the 85th percentile.

While lower food-at-home prices for some foods likely contribute to rising obesity rates, we cannot comment on the effects in comparison with other factors, such as prices of food-away-from-home, access to specific foods in schools, or availability of calorie content labels in restaurants and other eating places. Cross-sectional studies find that higher fast food prices are associated with lower adolescent BMI (Chou et al., 2008; Auld and Powell, 2009) and a lower probability of overweight (Powell et al., 2009).

Table 4. Estimation results, fixed effects, 1-year lagged prices, by gender, income group and race

BMI (Body Mass Index)	Boys	Girls	House-Hold income > 185% pov.	House-hold income 130-185% pov.	House-hold income <130% pov.	White	Black	Hispanic
Carbonated beverages	-0.058***	-0.023	-0.021	-0.085**	-0.051*	-0.031**	-0.032	-0.071**
	(0.016)	(0.016)	(0.014)	(0.037)	(0.026)	(0.015)	(0.032)	(0.030)
Fruit drinks	-0.007	-0.005	-0.011	0.008	-0.003	-0.001	0.023	-0.009
	(0.008)	(0.008)	(0.007)	(0.019)	(0.011)	(0.007)	(0.019)	(0.011)
100 percent juices	-0.027**	-0.034***	-0.022**	-0.040	-0.033**	-0.030***	-0.071***	-0.024
	(0.012)	(0.012)	(0.011)	(0.026)	(0.016)	(0.011)	(0.027)	(0.018)
Lowfat milk (skim, and 1%)	0.003	0.022*	0.019	0.022	0.010	0.012	-0.004	0.016
	(0.013)	(0.012)	(0.011)	(0.028)	(0.019)	(0.012)	(0.023)	(0.023)
Whole milk	0.010	0.008	0.007	0.017	-0.004	0.014	0.040	-0.021
	(0.013)	(0.012)	(0.012)	(0.030)	(0.019)	(0.011)	(0.030)	(0.023)

Table 4. (Continued)

BMI (Body Mass Index)	Boys	Girls	House-Hold income > 185% pov.	House-hold income 130-185% pov.	House-hold income <130% pov.	White	Black	Hispanic
Fresh and frozen dark green vegetables	-0.006	0.029**	0.009	-0.065**	0.021	-0.011	0.014	0.004
	(0.013)	(0.012)	(0.011)	(0.029)	(0.018)	(0.011)	(0.030)	(0.024)
Fresh and frozen starchy vegetables	-0.035***	-0.024**	-0.030***	-0.022	-0.014	-0.042***	-0.008	-0.025
	(0.009)	(0.010)	(0.008)	(0.023)	(0.015)	(0.008)	(0.021)	(0.018)
Sweet snacks	0.015	-0.009	-0.009	-0.012	0.015	-0.001	0.016	0.007
	(0.012)	(0.013)	(0.012)	(0.029)	(0.017)	(0.013)	(0.027)	(0.020)
Thrifty Food Plan basket	0.018	-0.040	-0.009	0.216***	-0.018	0.060**	0.016	0.013
	(0.033)	(0.033)	(0.028)	(0.071)	(0.050)	(0.028)	(0.079)	(0.061)
Number of observations	25,920	25,250	32,850	6,660	15,330	32,620	5,810	7,940
Number of children	7,700	7,390	10,520	4,120	6,900	9,040	2,040	2,510
R-squared (within)	0.694	0.727	0.701	0.709	0.723	0.708	0.734	0.731
R-squared (between)	0.136	0.125	0.177	0.251	0.209	0.126	0.151	0.142
R-squared (overall)	0.286	0.296	0.289	0.292	0.297	0.301	0.301	0.295

*** $p < 0.01$, ** $p < 0.05$, * $p < 0.1$

Notes: Number of observations is rounded to the nearest 10. Standard errors in parentheses are adjusted using Huber-White covariance matrix estimate. Fixed-effects control variables include the child's age (in months), household income (not for income subgroups), parent types, and survey round of data. Body Mass Index and all prices are in log scale.

Source: ERS estimates using data from the Early Childhood Longitudinal Study, Kindergarten Class of 1998-99 and the Quarterly Food-atHome Price Database.

REFERENCES

Andreyeva, T., M. Long, and K. Brownell. 2010. "The Impact of Food Prices on Consumption: A Systematic Review of Research on the Price Elasticity of Demand for Food." *American Journal of Public Health* 100: 216-222.

Auld, M.C., and L. Powell. 2009. "Economics of Food Energy Density and Adolescent Body Weight," *Economica* 72: 719-40.

Becker, G.S. 1965. "A Theory of the Allocation of Time," *Economic Journal* 75: 493-517.

Carlson, A., M. Lino, W.-Y. Juan, K. Hanson, and P.P. Basiotis. 2007. *Thrifty Food Plan, 2006*. CNPP-19. U.S. Department of Agriculture, Center for Nutrition Policy and Promotion.

Centers for Disease Control and Prevention (CDC). 2000. "Percentile Data Files with LMS Values." http://www.cdc.gov/growthcharts/percentile_ data_files.htm.

Chou, S.Y., I. Rashad, and M. Grossman. 2008. "Fast-food restaurant advertising on television and its influence on childhood obesity," *Journal of Law and Economics* 51: 599–618.

Chow, Carson C., and Kevin D. Hall. 2008. "The Dynamics of Human Body Weight Change," *PLoS Computational Biology* 4(3): e1000045. doi:10.1371/journal.pcbi.1000045.

Cole, T.J., M.S. Faith, A. Pietrobelli, and M. Heo. 2005. "What is the best measure of adiposity change in growing children: BMI, BMI %, BMI z-score or BMI centile?" *European Journal of Clinical Nutrition* 59: 419-425.

Finkelstein, E.A., J.G. Trogdon, J.W. Cohen, and W. Dietz. 2009. "Annual Medical Spending Attributable To Obesity: Payer-And Service-Specific Estimates," *Health Affairs* 28: 822-831.

Flegal, K., and R. Troiano. 2000. "Changes in the distribution of body mass index of adults and children in the US population," *International Journal of Obesity-Related Metabolic Disorders* 24: 807-18.

Kuchler, F., and H. Stewart. 2008. *Price Trends Are Similar for Fruits, Vegetables, and Snack Foods*. Economic Research Report Number 55, U.S. Department of Agriculture, Economic Research Service, March.

Institute of Medicine. 2008. "Nutrition Standards and Meal Requirements for National School Lunch and Breakfast Programs: Phase I. Proposed Approach for Recommending Revisions." V. Stallings and C. Taylor, eds. Washington, DC: National Academies Press.

Jolliffe, D. 2004. "Extent of overweight among U.S. children and adolescents from 1971 to 2000." *Journal of the International Association for the Study of Obesity* 28:4-9.

Must, A., and R. Strauss. 1999. "Risks and consequences of childhood and adolescent obesity," *International Journal of Obesity-Related Metabolic Disorders 23*: S2, 2-11.

Nielsen, S.J., and B. Popkin. 2004. "Changes in beverage intake between 1977 and 2001." *American Journal of Preventive Medicine* 27: 205-210.

Ogden, C., and M. Carroll. 2010. "Prevalence of Obesity Among Children and Adolescents: United States, Trends 1963–1965 Through 2007–2008." *Health E-Stat*. http://www.cdc.gov/nchs/fastats/overwt.htm

Powell, L., and Y. Bao. 2009. "Food prices, access to food outlets and child weight," *Economics and Human Biology* 7: 64-72.

Reedy, Jill, and Susan M. Krebs-Smith. 2010. "Dietary Sources of Energy, Solid Fats, and Added Sugars among Children and Adolescents in the United States," *Journal of the American Dietetic Association* 110: 1477-1484.

Senauer, B.. and M. Garcia. 1991. "Determinants of the Nutrition and Health Status of Preschool Children: An Analysis with Longitudinal Data," *Economic Development and Cultural Change* 39: 371-90.

Steinberger, J., A. Moran, C. Hong, D. Jacobs, and A. Sinaiko. 2001. "Adiposity in childhood predicts obesity and insulin resistance in young adulthood," *Journal of Pediatrics* 138: 469-73.

Sturm, R., and A. Datar. 2005. "Body mass index in elementary school children, metropolitan area food prices and food outlet density," *Public Health* 119:1059–68.

Sturm, R., and A. Datar. 2008. "Food prices and weight gain during elementary school: 5 year update," *Public Health* 122: 1140–43.

Sturm, R., L. Powell, J. Chriqui, and F. Chaloupka. 2010. "Soda Taxes, Soft Drink Consumption, and Children's Body Mass Index," *Health Affairs* 29: Web First.

Todd, Jessica E., Lisa Mancino, Ephraim Leibtag, and Christina Tripodo. 2010. *Methodology Behind the Quarterly Food-at-Home Price Database*, Technical Bulletin No. 1926, U.S. Dept. of Agriculture, Economic Research Service.

Todd, Jessica E., and Ephraim S. Leibtag. 2010. "New Database Shows Substantial Geographic Food Price Variation," *Amber Waves* (Data Feature), Vol. 8, Issue 3, Economic Research Service, U.S. Department of Agriculture, September 2010, p. 52-53.

Todd, Jessica E., Ephraim Leibtag and Corttney Penberthy. 2011. *Geographic Differences in the Relative Price of Healthy Foods*. EIB-78, U.S. Department of Agriculture, Economic Research Service, June.

Tourangeau, K, C. Nord, T. Le, S. Wan, and J. West. 2009. "Early Childhood Longitudinal Study, Kindergarten Class of 1998-99: User's Guide to the

Longitudinal Kindergarten-Eighth Grade Public-Use Data File," National Center for Education Statistics.

U.S. Department of Health and Human Services (U.S. DHHS). 2007. "The Surgeon General's Call to Action to Prevent and Decrease Overweight and Obesity." http://www.surgeongeneral.gov/topics/obesity/calltoaction/fact_adolescents.htm

Variyam, J., J. Blaylock, B. Lin, K. Ralston, and D. Smallwood. 1999. "Mother's nutrition knowledge and children's dietary intakes," *American Journal of Agricultural Economics* 81: 373–384.

Wang, G. and W. Dietz. 2002. "Economic Burden of Obesity in Youths Aged 6 to 17 Years: 1979-1999," *Pediatrics* 109: 1-6.

Wang, Y., S. Bleich, and S. Gortmaker. 2008. "Increasing Caloric Contribution From Sugar-Sweetened Beverages and 100% Fruit Juices Among US Children and Adolescents, 1988-2004," *Pediatrics* 121: e1604-e1614.

Whitaker, R.C., J.A. Wright, M.S. Pepe, K.D. Seidel, and W.H. Dietz. 1997. "Predicting Obesity in Young Adulthood from Childhood and Parental Obesity," *New England Journal of Medicine* 337: 869-73.

APPENDIX A: QUARTERLY FOOD-AT-HOME PRICE DATABASE MARKET GROUPS, 2002-06

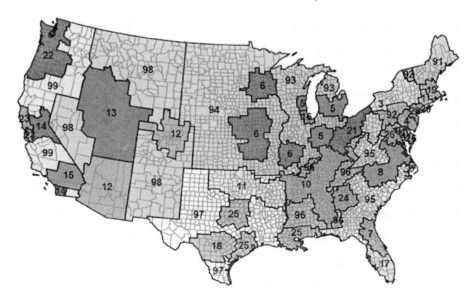

1 Hartford	13	Salt Lake City	25	Metro South 4
2 Urban NY	14	Metro California	26	Washington, DC
3 Western NY/PA	15	Los Angeles	91	Nonmetro New England
4 Philadelphia	16	Chicago	92	Nonmetro Middle Atlantic
5 Metro Midwest1	17	South Florida	93	Nonmetro East North Central
6 Metro Midwest2	18	San Antonio	94	Nonmetro West North Central
7 North Florida	19	Boston	95	Nonmetro South Atlantic
8 Metro South 1	20	Other NY	96	Nonmetro East South Central
9 Baltimore	21	Metro Ohio	97	Nonmetro West South Central
10 Metro South 2	22	North Pacific	98	Nonmetro Mountain
11 Metro South 3	23	San Francisco	99	Nonmetro Pacific
12 Metro Mountain	24	Atlanta		

Notes: For 1999-2001, market 81 is composed of markets 91 and 92; market 82 is composed of markets 93 and 94; market 83 is composed of markets 95, 96, and 97; and market 84 is composed of markets 98 and 99.

Source: Todd et al. (2010).

APPENDIX B: CONSTRUCTION OF THE THRIFTY FOOD PLAN WEEKLY COST

The Thrifty Food Plan (TFP) identifies quantities (in pounds) of foods as purchased that will allow an individual or family to consume a healthy diet (one that meets the dietary guidelines) at a low cost. The cost of the TFP is used to determine the maximum Supplemental Nutrition Assistance Program (SNAP) benefit, but is estimated at the national level only. Here, we document how we calculated the average cost of the TFP basket for a family of four (two adults, age 19-50, one child age 6-8 and one child age 9-11) for each quarter and an average for the year in each Quarterly Food-at-Home Price Database (QFAHPD) market group.

There is not a perfect correspondence between the TFP food categories and the QFAHPD categories. For example, the TFP includes fresh, frozen, and canned forms in its total pounds of dark green vegetables, while the QFAHPD includes market prices for fresh and frozen dark green vegetables and another set of prices for canned dark green vegetables. In such cases, we compute the national expenditure share on each form within a category. The price for the TFP category is then the weighted average of the QFAHPD prices, weighted by that national expenditure shares.

In other cases, the TFP identifies quantities for groups that are not identified in the QFAHPD (such as popcorn and other whole-grain snacks). In these cases, we use the QFAHPD price that is most similar (in this case, salty snacks) to serve as the price for the TFP category.

A few of the TFP categories that are not priced in the QFAHPD are excluded from our calculations of the TFP. These include coffee and tea, dry soups, and gravies, sauces, and condiments. A list of the comparisons is at the end of this appendix.

The TFP lists the pounds of each food category for various age/gender groups, from which we determine the total for our family of four. The total TFP weekly cost is simply the sum of the costs of each food category, calculated by multiplying the total pounds needed times the price per pound.

Since the QFAHPD provides average market group prices and not necessarily the lowest available prices, our estimates of the cost of the TFP may be higher than the minimum required to purchase a healthy diet. However, because the basket identifies a nutritionally adequate diet that meets the Dietary Guidelines, we feel that this metric is useful to compare costs of a fixed basket of foods over time.

Appendix Table B1. Thrifty Food Plan (TFP) categories and corresponding Quarterly Food-at-Home-Price Database (QFAHPD) food groups

TFP category	QFAHPD food groups
Whole fruits	Fresh and frozen whole fruit; canned fruit
Fruit juices	Fruit juice
Dark green vegetables	Fresh and frozen dark green vegetables; canned dark green vegetables
Orange vegetables	Fresh and frozen orange vegetables; canned orange vegetables
All potato products	Fresh and frozen starchy vegetables; canned starchy vegetables
Other vegetables	Fresh and frozen other vegetables with select nutrients; canned vegetables with select nutrients; fresh and frozen other vegetables; canned other veg-etables
Canned and dry beans/legumes	Fresh and frozen legumes; canned legumes
Whole grain breads, pasta, flours, cereals, and snacks	Whole grain packaged products; whole grain flours and mixes; frozen ready-to-cook whole grains
Refined grain breads, pasta, cereals, flours,	Refined-grain packaged products; refined-grain flours and mixes; frozen
pies, pastries, and snacks	ready-to-cook refined grains, commercially prepared baking mixes, ready-to-eat bakery items, commercially prepared packaged snacks
Lower fat and skim milk and yogurt	Lowfat and skim milk; low fat yogurt
Whole fat milk, yogurt, and cream	Whole and 2% milk, whole-milk yogurt; other whole-fat dairy products
Milk drinks and milk desserts	Frozen ice cream and other frozen desserts

Appendix Table B1. (Continued)

TFP category	QFAHPD food groups
All cheese	Lowfat cheese; regular fat cheese
Beef, pork, veal, lamb, bacon, sausages, and lunch meats	Fresh and frozen low-fat meat; fresh and frozen regular fat meat; canned meat
Chicken, turkey, and game birds	Fresh and frozen poultry; canned poultry
Fish and fish products	Fresh and frozen fish; canned fish
Nuts, nut butters, and seeds	Raw nuts and seeds; processed nuts and nut butters
Eggs	Eggs
Table fats and oils	Oils; solid fats
Soft drinks, sodas, fruit drinks, and ades	Carbonated soft drinks; noncarbonated fruit drinks and ades
Sugars, sweets, and candies	Raw sugars and sweeteners; packaged sweet snacks
Frozen or refrigerated entrees	Frozen entrees
Soups (ready-to-serve and condensed)	Canned soups and sauces

TFP categories not included in QFAHPD price estimate:

Gravies, sauces, and condiments

Coffee and tea

Soups (dry).

End Notes

[1] According to the CDC definitions, overweight children age 2 to 19 have BMI-for-age between the 85th and 95th percentiles in the BMI-for-age and gender growth charts, obese children have BMI-for-age at or above the 95th percentile in the BMI-for-age and gender growth charts. BMI is defined as the ratio of weight (in kilograms) over height (in meters) squared. It can also be expressed as weight (in pounds) divided by height (in inches) squared and multiplied by 703.

[2] In constant (2001) dollar value.

[3] Includes fresh, canned, and frozen categories.

[4] This price structure does not take into account either the quality or variety of fresh fruits and vegetables, which have improved over the last 30 years. See Kuchler and Stewart (2008) for more details.

[5] Although substitution both within and across food groups could influence how these price effects translate into weight changes.

[6] We merged two waves of data that were collected in the fall and spring of the kindergarten year to form the first round of data in our analysis.

[7] The QFAHPD can be downloaded at <http://www.ers.usda.gov/Data/qfahpd/ index.htm>

[8] Due to rules regarding access and use of restricted data, all numbers of observations in this report are rounded to the nearest 10.

[9] We also estimated our model using standardized continuous BMI (z-scores) and percentiles in the BMI-for-age distributions as the dependent variable. The continuous BMI scores are provided by ECLS-K. BMI z-scores are calculated based on the 2000 CDC Growth

Reference. BMI percentiles are calculated by normalizing the z-scores. These are standard measures of children's BMI that are used in previous research. Each measure has its advantages and disadvantages. For detailed discussion, see Cole et al. (2005). The results are consistent and comparable to our main measure.

[10] The ECLS-K did not sample in Alaska.

[11] A Hausman test rejected a random-effects model with a chi-square value of 146.55 and 24 degrees of freedom

[12] In addition, Chow and Hall (2008) find that changes in weight are not necessarily constant over time (linear).

[13] We also test the sensitivity of our specification by clustering at the county level, and the results are not affected.

[14] As a further robustness check, we also estimated a model where the 4th quarter lag price is replaced with the average price of the 4th-7th previous quarters, and found qualitatively and quantitatively similar results (results available upon request).

[15] Because the quantile regression examines the relationship between the independent variables and conditional quantiles of the independent variable, not percentiles in the BMI growth charts, the 85th quantile translates to approximately the 95th percentile in the BMI growth charts. Note that about 16 percent of the sample can be classified as overweight (over the 85th percentile in BMI-for-age).

In: Weighty Factors in Children's Food...   ISBN: 978-1-62257-917-4
Editors: C.E. Oyler and C. De Volld   © 2013 Nova Science Publishers, Inc.

Chapter 2

HOW FOOD AWAY FROM HOME AFFECTS CHILDREN'S DIET QUALITY[*]

Lisa Mancino, Jessica E. Todd, Joanne Guthrie and Biing-Hwan Lin

ABSTRACT

Based on 2 days of dietary data and panel data methods, this study includes estimates of how each child's consumption of food away from home, food from school (which includes all foods available for purchase at schools, not only those offered as part of USDA reimbursable meals), and caloric sweetened beverages affects that child's diet quality and calorie consumption. Compared with meals and snacks prepared at home, food prepared away from home increases caloric intake of children, especially older children. Each food-away-from-home meal adds 108 more calories to daily total intake among children ages 13-18 than a snack or meal from home; all food from school is estimated to add 145 more calories. Both food away from home and all food from school also lower the daily diet quality of older children (as measured by the 2005 Healthy Eating Index). Among younger children, who are more likely than older children to eat a USDA school meal and face a more healthful school food environment, the effect of food from school on caloric intake and diet quality does not differ significantly from that of food from home.

---

[*] This is an edited, reformatted and augmented edition of a United States Department of Agriculture Economic Research Service publication, Report ERR-104, dated October 2010.

Keywords: Food away from home (FAFH), food from school (FFS), caloric sweetened beverages (CSB), children's diet quality, 2005 Healthy Eating Index (HEI-2005), fixed effects, first difference, Continuing Survey of Food Intakes by Individuals (CSFII), National Health and Nutrition Examination Survey (NHANES), ERS, USDA

ACKNOWLEDGMENTS

The authors thank the following reviewers for their insightful suggestions and comments: Ronette Briefel (Mathematica Policy Research), Hayden Stewart (USDA, Economic Research Service (ERS)), Mary Story (Division of Epidemiology and Community Health at the University of Minnesota), and Steven Carlson and Jay Hirschman (USDA, Food and Nutrition Service). John Weber and Cynthia A. Ray of ERS provided editorial and design assistance.

SUMMARY

In recent decades, more and more American children have become over-weight, and most now eat a low-quality diet—consuming too much calorie-dense, low-nutrient foods and too little fruits, vegetables, whole grains, and milk. Increased consumption of foods prepared outside the home has been identified as a possible cause of rising rates of obesity and poor diet quality.

What is the issue?

Among children ages 6-18, away-from-home foods are most likely to come from fast food outlets, restaurants, and schools. Increased consumption of such foods may be a cause of overweight, or it may just be correlated with other factors that increase risk of overweight, such as individual food prefer-ences and access to myriad food outlets. Consumption of caloric sweetened beverages, which is associated with both overweight and eating out, may contribute to the effects of away-from-home foods on caloric intake and diet quality. In this study, previous research is advanced through an examination of the effects of both commercially prepared food away from home and all food from school on the diets of children, where all food from school includes foods available for purchase at schools, not only those offered as part of USDA reimbursable meals. Also, researchers separate the effects of caloric sweetened beverage consumption from the effects of away-from-home meals. The results may help to inform obesity prevention policies and strategies.

What are the Findings?

Food obtained from fast food outlets, restaurants, and other commercial sources is associated with increased caloric intake and lower diet quality, as measured by the Healthy Eating Index (HEI), especially among children ages 13-18. These effects hold after employing a methodology that controls for the impacts of underlying personal characteristics and circumstances, such as access to food outlets, which might also affect food choices. This finding strengthens the argument that there is a causal relationship between food away from home and both increased caloric consumption and decreased dietary quality. It also supports policy and educational efforts to improve children's choices of away-from-home foods and beverages.

Consumption of caloric sweetened beverages when eating meals or snacks obtained at commercial food establishments or at school contributes to the adverse dietary effects of food away from home. About 35 percent of the caloric increase associated with food away from home is attributable to caloric sweetened beverages, as is 20 percent of the decline in HEI scores. Nevertheless, after controlling for the effects of consumption of caloric sweetened beverages, researchers find that, for all children, each away-from-home meal adds 65 calories and lowers diet quality scores by 4 percent, compared with meals prepared at home. For older children, the effect amounts to 107 additional calories for each away-from-home meal. These results suggest that food away from home and caloric sweetened beverages each contribute to the overall quantity and quality of the foods children consume.

The effects of food from school also differ between younger and older children. Again controlling for intake of caloric sweetened beverages, researchers find that consumption of all food from school does not appear to have negative effects on the diets of younger children (ages 6-13). However, among children ages 13-18, all food from school has effects similar to those of food away from home, increasing daily caloric intake by 145 calories and lowering diet quality scores by 3 percent, compared with food prepared at home. Older children and adolescents tend to consume more meals and snacks from all away-from-home sources than younger children. Thus, efforts to improve the quality of food away from home and food from school may especially benefit the older age group.

How was the Study Conducted?

Analysis is based on dietary recall data from the 2003-04 National Health and Nutrition Examination Survey and the 1994-96 Continuing Survey of Food Intakes by Individuals. Researchers used 2 days of dietary intake data from school-age children (ages 6-18) to obtain first-difference estimates of the effects of individual changes in the number of meals or snacks from foods prepared outside the home—from restaurants, fast food vendors and other commercial sources, or schools and day care centers—on diet quality. First-differencing, which controls for many personal characteristics and omits a great deal of selection bias, is also used to determine the effects of changes in consumption of caloric sweetened beverages on diet quality. Controlling for changes in beverage consumption provides a clearer picture of how food sources affect diet quality. Measures of diet quality include changes in total daily caloric intake, total daily HEI scores, and daily HEI component densities, such as fruit and vegetable cup equivalents per 1,000 calories of intake.

INTRODUCTION

In the last 30 years, the prevalence of obesity among children and adolescents in the United States has more than doubled for all age groups and tripled among those ages 12-19 (CDC, 2009). Childhood obesity is associated with increased risk of Type 2 diabetes, sleep apnea, high blood pressure and cholesterol, as well as negative social, emotional, and academic outcomes (Gable et al., 2008). In addition, estimates suggest overweight children face a 70-percent chance of becoming overweight or obese adults, putting them at increased risk of suffering numerous obesity-related health problems later in life (USDHHS, 2007).

The prevention of childhood obesity has therefore become a major public health objective (Healthy People 2010). In searching for the causes of rising childhood obesity, researchers have identified increased consumption of food prepared away from home as a potential culprit. Like adults, children today eat a larger share of their daily calories from foods prepared outside the home than they did 30 years ago. In 1977-78, the average child age 2-17 obtained 20 percent of his or her daily calories from food away from home (FAFH) (Guthrie et al., 2002). Analysis of 2003-06 data from the National Health and Nutrition Examination Survey (NHANES) finds that, on average, children today get roughly 35 percent of their calories from FAFH. Guthrie et al. (2002) find that FAFH is of lower nutritional quality than food prepared at home, having more fat and saturated fat and less dietary fiber, calcium, and iron. Unsurprisingly, many studies find that energy intake is higher and diet quality is lower among children who eat FAFH (particularly fast food) than among those who do not (see Bowman and Vinyard, 2004; French et al., 2001; Sebastian et al., 2009). Findings in other studies suggest that overweight or obese children may consume more FAFH (see Gills and Bar-Or, 2003).

The consumption of FAFH, however, may not be a direct cause of poor diet quality and weight gain. Instead, it may just be linked to these outcomes through other factors, such as family time constraints, access to various food outlets, and preferences for certain foods. In other words, it is likely that FAFH consumption, diet quality, and weight are all shaped by these other factors. An analysis of adult diets shows that not controlling for such unobservable factors could overestimate the effect of FAFH on energy intake by as much as 25 percent (Mancino et al., 2009). As such, the potential impact of targeting FAFH as a means to curb childhood obesity may be overstated as well.

The objective of this study is to investigate whether consumption of FAFH directly affects children's energy intake and diet quality. We use a fixed- effects estimator on 2 days of dietary recall data to isolate the effects of consumption of FAFH from unobserved fixed characteristics that are likely correlated with FAFH consumption. In contrast to previous work, we define FAFH as all food not prepared at home and separate food obtained from school (FFS) cafeterias from all other FAFH.

This is an important distinction, as children are likely to have a different range of food options in schools than in other food-away-from-home establishments. Moreover, policy levers for influencing food choices at schools differ from those available for influencing food choices at restaurants, fast food establishments, and other sources of food prepared away from home. Lunches and breakfasts served in schools as part of the USDA school meal programs are subject to nutrition standards established by USDA. These standards could be modified in response to recent recommendations from the National Academy of Sciences' Institute of Medicine (IOM) (see IOM, 2009) or as part of Federal obesity prevention policies. Even foods and beverages sold outside the USDA school meal programs from snack bars and other sources (popularly referred to as "competitive foods" because they compete with USDA school meals) may be limited either by Federal, State, or local school policies. USDA now requires schools that participate in the USDA school meal programs to develop "wellness policies" that set standards for all foods and beverages sold in school. Many schools are trying to offer a more healthful mix of foods, sometimes by banning sales of competitive foods or limiting the types of these foods that can be sold. In addition, 31 States now have policies limiting access to or setting nutrition standards for competitive foods (Trust For America's Health, 2009).

In contrast, the policy options for altering food choices by children in restaurants, fast food establishments, and other commercial sources focus less on sales restrictions and more on informational efforts. Nutrition labeling on menus and other efforts to educate consumers may encourage parents—and some children—to change the way they typically select from among different types of foods and beverages. The shift in consumer demand that may result could also spur FAFH establishments to introduce more healthful menu options for children.

Given these differences in policy levers, it is important to disentangle the dietary effects of consuming school food from the effects of consuming other foods prepared away from home. Therefore, we separate them in our analysis and hereafter refer to food obtained at school as food from school (FFS) and food obtained from other sources as food away from home (FAFH).

We estimate the effects of an increase in the number of meals from FAFH and FFS on caloric intake and diet quality. Estimates are made for the entire sample of school-age children (ages 6-18)[1] and separately for younger children (ages 6-12) and adolescents (ages 13-18). We also test whether the effects of FAFH differ significantly from the effects of FFS and whether the effects of FAFH and FFS have changed between the two periods for which data are available: 1994-96 and 2003-04.

Additionally, we investigate the extent to which the effects of FAFH and FFS on diet quality are driven by the consumption of caloric sweetened beverages (CSB). Children's consumption of CSBs, such as carbonated soft drinks, fruit drinks, and sport drinks, has risen in recent years (Wang et al., 2008) and now accounts for close to 10 percent of total caloric intake for this age group. As with the effects of consumption of FAFH and FFS, researchers hypothesize that increased consumption of CSBs is associated with the rise in obesity (see Malik et al., 2006; Vartanian et al., 2007). CSBs often accompany FAFH meals and are commonly available in vending machines in schools. Thus, it is possible that some of the effects attributed to FAFH and FFS could be driven by an association with consumption of CSBs. We therefore control for CSB consumption to investigate whether this association changes the magnitude of the estimated relationship between diet quality and food source. Findings provide additional insight into the effects of food sources on children's diets and weight status and can help inform strategies for the prevention of childhood obesity.

PREVIOUS RESEARCH ON FOOD AWAY FROM HOME

Research on the role of FAFH on children's weight status, energy intake, and diet quality has focused primarily on the correlations of these measures with either fast food consumption or availability, as measured by distance or price. A number of studies show that children who eat fast food or fried foods away from home more frequently than other children also consume more energy, caloric sweetened beverages, and fat while also consuming less milk and fewer fruits and vegetables (see Bowman et al., 2004; French et al., 2001; Paeratakul et al., 2003; Sebastian et al., 2009). Some evidence suggests that children who are overweight or obese eat FAFH more frequently and consume more total energy when doing so than healthy-weight children (see Gillis and Bar-Or, 2003; Ebbeling et al., 2004).

Among studies focused on correlations between body weight and access to restaurants and fast food establishments, some find that proximity to restaurants has little to no effect on children's weight (see Burdette and Whitaker, 2004; Sturm and Datar, 2005). Currie et al. (2009), however, find that having a fast food restaurant within one-tenth of a mile of a school correlates with increased weight gain and obesity among schoolchildren. Powell and Bao (2009) also find that the relationship between local fast food prices and elevated Body Mass Index (BMI) is more pronounced among low-income adolescents, who may have greater access to FAFH (Block et al., 2004) than the general population.

While demonstrating a strong correlation between either FAFH consumption or FAFH availability and specific outcomes, such as overweight/obesity and lower diet quality, these studies do not confirm that FAFH is a cause of these outcomes. As stated earlier, FAFH consumption is influenced by many of the same factors that affect both diet quality and body weight. Similarly, the use of FAFH access as a means to identify consumption poses two potential problems. First, the cited studies lack data on actual FAFH intake or purchases. Thus, there is no guarantee that any correlation between weight gain and FAFH access is due to increased FAFH consumption. Second, retailers choose to locate in areas with high demand. Because the demand for FAFH is driven by the same factors that influence diet quality and body weight, access is arguably an endogenous variable.

SCHOOL MEALS AND OTHER FOOD OBTAINED AT SCHOOL

Given the important contribution of food obtained at school to the everyday diets of children, the effects of such foods on children's diets is of interest to researchers. Schools, like other nonhome food sources, now offer a more extensive and varied mix of eating options than in past decades. As of 2008, USDA school meal programs served 30.9 million lunches and 10.6 million breakfasts on an average schoolday. For participants, lunch contributes 31 percent of daily calories, whereas breakfast contributes 22 percent (Gordon et al., 2007). Nearly all children who eat school breakfast also eat school lunch; for such children, school meals may account for approximately half of their daily caloric intake.

USDA-sponsored meals are expected to meet Federal nutrition standards. And while most schools serve meals that meet standards for protein, vitamins, and minerals, many schools provide meals that exceed standards for fat and saturated fat and are also high in sodium[2] (Crepinsek et al., 2009). Other foods and beverages are also widely available in schools from vending machines, school stores and snack bars, or cafeterias, where they are sold as a la carte items. Overall, 40 percent of schoolchildren eat some type of competitive food or beverage on a given day (Fox et al., 2009). These competitive foods make up, on average, 13 percent of total daily calories for younger children and 15 percent for high schoolers. Competitive foods are not subject to the same Federal nutrition standards as foods that make up USDA meals. They tend to be low-nutrient, energy-dense foods, such as CSBs, high-fat baked goods, and desserts (Fox et al., 2009). As children age, their access to competitive foods expands and their consumption of USDA school lunches declines[3] (Fox et al., 2009). In addition, school lunch program meals appear to differ in quality by grade level, with meals served to secondary students being higher in fat than meals served to elementary students (Newman et al., 2009). The combination of less nutritious National School Lunch Program (NSLP) meals and more exposure to competitive foods may explain why previous research found that the positive qualities of foods consumed at school decline as students age (see Lin et al., 2001).

Despite these shortcomings, school meals are found to have several positive effects on students' diets, with program participants significantly more likely than nonparticipants to consume milk, fruit, and vegetables at lunchtime and less likely to eat desserts and snack items (Briefel et al., 2009). Intakes of CSBs at lunch by program participants are sufficiently lower than those of nonparticipants, resulting in a lower overall daily CSB intake (Briefel et al., 2009). However, as with the effects of FAFH, it is difficult to establish a causal relationship between school foods and diet quality because many of the same factors that influence school meal choice, such as food preferences and parental time constraints, also shape diet quality and body weight.

CALORIC SWEETENED BEVERAGES

Over the past three decades, children's beverage choices have registered a noticeable trend. Consumption of milk has declined, while consumption of carbonated soft drinks and fruit drinks has risen (table 1). Consumption of CSBs has also risen in recent years (Wang et al., 2009) and now makes up close to 10 percent of total caloric intake for this age group. Increased consumption of CSBs raises two concerns. First, it may displace consumption of more nutrient-rich beverages, such as low-fat milk. Second, rather than serving as a substitute for other foods and beverages, it may add calories to the diet, increasing the risk of obesity. Physiological research finds that self-compensation for calories consumed as certain liquids, such as CSBs, is imprecise and thus increases the likelihood of an individual's consuming excess calories (Mattes, 1996). Ludwig et al. (2001) find that in a sample of school-age children, over a 19-month period, CSB consumption is associated with increased risk of becoming overweight. Two recent reviews of the literature conclude that CSB consumption is linked with increased risk of obesity and diabetes (see Malik et al., 2006; Vartanian et al., 2007). It is noted that CSBs often accompany FAFH meals and, during the time data were collected for this study, they were commonly available in vending machines in schools (CDC, 2006; Briefel et al., 2009). Clearly, obesity, FAFH, FFS, and CSB consumption are linked, making it very challenging to sort out the specific effects that each may have on obesity.

**Table 1. Daily Per Capita Consumption of Beverages
Among Children Ages 2-18**

Beverage	1977-78	1994-96	2003-06
	Ounces		
Nondiet soft drinks	4.61	8.94	9.39
Fruit drinks	3.03	5.07	5.66
Milk	14.77	11.30	9.60

Source: USDA, Economic Research Service analysis of Continuing Survey of Food
Intakes of Individuals and National Health and Nutrition Examination Survey
first-day dietary recall data.

**Table 2. Intake Densities Corresponding to Maximum Component Score
in HEI-2005 Measure**

HEI-2005 component	Intake for maximum score
Total fruit	≥ 0.8 cup equivalents
Whole fruit	≥ 0.4 cup equivalents
Whole grains	≥ 1.5 oz. equivalents
Milk	≥ 1.3 cup equivalents
Total vegetable	≥ 1.1 cup equivalents
Dark-green, orange vegetables	≥ 0.4 cup equivalents
Saturated fat[*]	≤ 7 percent
Sodium	≤ 700 milligrams
Extra calories[*]	≤ 20 percent

Note: *Intake is percent of total energy; otherwise, densities are per 1,000 kcal. HEI =
Healthy Eating Index.
Source: USDA, Economic Research Service using data from Guenther et al. (2007).

DATA AND SAMPLE

We use data from two nationally representative surveys covering the
periods 1994-96 and 2003-04. The Continuing Survey of Food Intakes by
Individuals (CSFII) collected 2 nonconsecutive days of dietary recall data
between 1994 and 1996 for a sample of adults and children. Both days of
intake data were collected through interviews with survey participants. The
National Health and Nutrition Examination Survey, conducted by the Centers
for Disease Control and Prevention, expanded intake data collection from 1

day to 2 days in 2002 but only began releasing both days of dietary intake in 2003. Because USDA managed the dietary intake component for both surveys, many of the questions, such as those asking where foods were eaten and obtained, are the same in both surveys. This facilitates combining the two surveys together and allows us to link responses to the appropriate MyPyramid Equivalents databases (MPED) (Friday and Bowman, 2006; Bowman et al., 2008) and, consequently, calculate the 2005 Healthy Eating Index (HEI-2005) scores. The 2003-04 NHANES is the most recent dataset containing 2 days of dietary intake for which the HEI-2005 can be constructed.[4] As will be described in more detail, the index is based on per calorie intake and thus supports comparison of intakes that vary in quantity. We limit our sample to school- age children between ages 6 and 18.

We examine the effects of FAFH, FFS, and CSB consumption on aggregate and specific measures of diet quality. The aggregate measures are total daily caloric (energy) intake and total HEI-2005 score. Excessive energy intake is a main factor in weight gain. The HEI-2005, developed by USDA's Center for Nutrition Policy and Promotion (CNPP), is an index that measures how well an individual's diet adheres to the 2005 *Dietary Guidelines for Americans* (see USDHHS/USDA 2005; Guenther et al., 2008). The total score is the sum of an individual's scores on 12 components: total fruit; whole fruit; total vegetables; dark-green and orange vegetables and legumes; total grains; whole grains; milk; meat and beans; oils; saturated fat; sodium; and extra calories from solid fat and added sugar (extra calories). The *Dietary Guidelines* recommend consuming at least a minimum amount for the first nine components and consuming no more than a maximum amount for the last three components, while also balancing daily caloric intake with daily caloric expenditure.

These component scores are created using a density approach. For fruit, vegetables, grains, milk, meat, and beans, densities reflect the number of cups or ounce equivalents per 1,000 calories consumed by an individual daily. For oils and sodium, the densities measure the grams and milligrams consumed per 1,000 calories, respectively. For saturated fat and extra calories, densities measure the share of an individual's daily caloric consumption. This analysis focuses specifically on measures of the component densities for which current dietary intake is lacking—total fruit, whole fruit, total vegetables, dark-green and orange vegetables, whole grains, and milk—and is excessive—saturated fat, sodium, and extra calories (Guenther et al., 2008; Fungwe et al., 2009). Table 2 summarizes the intake corresponding to a maximum score for each of these components in the HEI-2005.

Following the approach used in Todd et al. (2010), in this study, eating occasions are classified as FAFH based on the source from which respondents report each food was obtained. Regardless of where the foods were consumed, foods obtained from fast food or table service restaurants are classified as FAFH.[5] Foods obtained from a school cafeteria or day care center are identified as FFS.[6] The FFS classification includes any food sold at school—those sold as part of the USDA school meals as well as competitive foods sold a la carte. Meals that contain foods from multiple sources are classified based on the source of the food (excluding beverages) that accounts for the majority of the meal's calories. For example, if a student reports eating a lunch or breakfast from school and a dessert from home, the eating occasion is identified as a food from school meal as long as the food from school provides more than 50 percent of the calories consumed during that meal. The final category, food at home (FAH), comprises the remaining food sources. The majority (97 percent) of foods classified as FAH come from some sort of grocery store or from someone else, such as a dinner prepared by a friend. Meals are classified as breakfast, lunch, dinner, or snack based on the respondent's stated definition of the eating occasion.

Beverages are classified using the USDA eight-digit food-code descriptors in the CSFII and NHANES. Regardless of where a respondent obtained a beverage, if the product contained some sort of caloric sweetener, such as sugar or corn syrup, it is classified as a caloric sweetened beverage. Specifically, the caloric sweetened beverages defined as CSBs come from one of the following categories—fruit or fruit-flavored drinks, energy drinks, flavored water, coffees, teas, and nonalcoholic, or "virgin," beverages, such as nonalcoholic wines and beers.

Based on an approach that uses Stata 10.1 to account for sampling weights and incorporate survey design, sample means are reported in table 3 for the explanatory and dependent variables for the full sample of children. The table includes both the 2-day mean as well as the 2-day difference for each variable for the pooled sample (both the 1994-96 and 2003-04 surveys). Average daily caloric intake for children is nearly 2,124 calories, with an average difference between the 2 days of nearly 114 calories. The mean HEI-2005 score is less than 50 (out of a maximum of 100), and the average daily variation is less than 1 (0.34). Average intake of milk per 1,000 calories comes closest to the recommended amount (1.03 cup equivalents versus 1.3 cup equivalents for a maximum component score). For other components in which average intake is below the level corresponding to the maximum HEI-2005 score, the deficits range from 40 percent (whole fruit) to 90 percent (dark-green and orange vegetables). For components in which intake is above the recommended levels, consumption exceeds recommendations by 66 percent for saturated fat, 92 percent for extra calories, and 114 percent for sodium.

Table 3. Summary Statistics, Children Ages 6-18, 1994-96 and 2003-04 Pooled

Dependent variables	Two-day means		Two-day differences (day 2 - day 1)	
	2-day means		2-day differences	
	Mean	SE of mean	Mean	SE of mean
Daily energy intake (kcal)	2,124.12	18.36	-113.60	17.19
HEI-2005	48.66	0.34	0.57	0.59
Total fruit density (cup equiv. per 1,000 kcal)	0.49	0.01	0.01	0.02
Whole fruit density (cup equiv. per 1,000 kcal)	0.24	0.01	0.02	0.01
Whole grain density (ounce equiv. per 1,000 kcal)	0.28	0.01	0.00	0.01
Dairy density (cup equiv. per 1,000 kcal)	1.03	0.02	0.02	0.02
Vegetable density (cup equiv. per 1,000 kcal)	0.56	0.01	0.02	0.02
Dark-green, orange density (cup equiv. per 1,000 kcal)	0.04	0.00	0.01	0.00
Percent saturated fat (percent of energy)	11.62	0.06	-0.04	0.10
Sodium density (milligrams per 1,000 kcal)	1,570.98	8.66	26.41	13.00
Percent of energy from extra calories	38.43	0.26	-0.95	0.37
Explanatory variables				
Breakfast—1 respondent ate breakfast; 0 otherwise	0.81	0.01	0.03	0.01
Lunch—1 respondent ate lunch; 0 otherwise	0.83	0.01	0.04	0.01
Dinner—1 respondent ate dinner; 0 otherwise	0.93	0.00	0.00	0.01
Snack (number)	1.39	0.02	-0.22	0.02
Number of meals away from home	0.50	0.01	-0.07	0.02
Number of meals from foods sold at school	0.32	0.02	-0.02	0.02
Caloric sweetened beverages consumed (grams)	559.51	12.59	-66.05	12.53
Weekend—1 recall occurred on a weekend; 0 otherwise	0.30	0.01	0.01	0.00
Demographic subgroups				
Male	0.52	0.01	n/a	n/a
NHANES (observed in 2003-04)	0.52	0.02	n/a	n/a

Note: The pooled sample size is 5,285: 1994-96 is 2,690 and 2003-04 is 2,595. Weighted means reported; Stata 10.1 is used to incorporate the complex survey design adjust the standard errors. Sample includes only children who reported 2 days of dietary intake data.
NHANES = National Health and Nutrition Examination Survey. n/a = not applicable.
Source: USDA, Economic Research Service.

Table 4. Summary Statistics by Age Group, 1994-96 and 2003-04 Pooled Data

Dependent variables	Children ages 6 to 12 (n=2,677)			Children ages 13 to 18 (n=2,608)	
	Mean	SE		Mean	SE
Daily energy intake (kcal)	1,996.67	23.74		2,269.10	32.27
HEI-2005	49.75	0.46		47.43	0.35
Total fruit density (cup equiv. per 1,000 kcal)	0.54	0.02		0.43	0.02
Whole fruit density (cup equiv. per 1,000 kcal)	0.29	0.01		0.19	0.01
Whole grain density (ounce equiv. per 1,000 kcal)	0.32	0.01		0.23	0.01
Dairy density (cup equiv. per 1,000 kcal)	1.13	0.02		0.91	0.03
Vegetable density (cup equiv. per 1,000 kcal)	0.53	0.01		0.60	0.01
Dark-green, orange density (cup equiv. per 1,000 kcal)	0.04	0.00		0.04	0.00
Percent saturated fat (percent of energy)	11.74	0.08		11.47	0.09
Sodium density (milligrams per 1,000 kcal)	1,556.48	11.22		1,587.48	11.73
Percent of energy from extra calories	37.90	0.28		39.03	0.35
Explanatory variables					
Breakfast	0.88	0.01		0.73	0.01
Lunch	0.88	0.01		0.77	0.01
Dinner	0.95	0.00		0.91	0.01
Snack	1.43	0.03		1.34	0.03
Number of meals away from home	0.40	0.01		0.61	0.02
Number of meals at school	0.38	0.02		0.25	0.02
Caloric sweetened beverages consumed (grams)	420.86	12.18		717.24	19.08
Dietary recall occurred on the weekend	0.30	.008	0.01	0.00	0.30
Demographic subgroups					
Male	0.52	0.01		0.51	0.01
NHANES (observed in 2003-04)	0.51	0.02		0.53	0.02

Note: Weighted means reported; Stata 10.1 is used to incorporate the complex survey design adjust the standard errors. Samples include only children who reported 2 days of dietary intake data. NHANES = National Health and Nutrition Examination Survey. HEI = Healthy Eating Index.

Source: USDA, Economic Research Service.

Because past research shows that the healthfulness of the school food environment declines as students progress through the school system (see Finkelstein et al., 2008; Briefel et al., 2009), we separate children into two age groups: those in elementary school (ages 6-12) and those in middle and high school (ages 13-18). Table 4 presents sample means for each subgroup of children. As expected, older children consume more calories per day but consume less fruit, whole grains, and milk. Younger children are less likely to skip meals and more likely to consume snacks and eat more meals from food from school. In contrast, older children consume more meals from food away from home. Older children also consume more caloric sweetened beverages (68 percent more than younger children).

ESTIMATION APPROACH

Estimates Using the Pooled Data

One common approach to estimating the effect of FAFH and FFS on diet quality is to treat them as an exogenous, explanatory variable and estimate a regression of the following form:

$$DQ_i = \alpha + \beta X_i + \gamma FAFH_i + \theta FFS_i + \mu_i + \varepsilon_i \tag{1}$$

where DQ is a measure of diet quality for individual i; X is a vector of control variables, such as age and gender; FAFH is the number of meals from FAFH; FFS is the number of meals from school; μ_i is a vector of relevant unobservable factors, such as food preferences, parental time constraints, and access to various food outlets; and ε_i is a stochastic error term.

However, as has been argued, FAFH and FFS consumption are driven by many of the same unobservable variables in ì. Not controlling for this relationship between ì and either FAFH or FFS will bias estimates of ã and è. To obtain unbiased estimates, one must separate the choice of FAFH and FFS from the relevant unobservable factors in ì. Leveraging the fact that the number of meals eaten away from home or obtained from school may vary across the 2 days of intake, one can isolate the effects of FAFH and FFS from the factors in ì that are fixed over time by estimating a regression on the differences between days:

$$DQ_{i2} - DQ_{i1} = (\alpha - \alpha) + \beta(\mathbf{X}_i - \mathbf{X}_i) + \gamma(FAFH_{i2} + FAFH_{i1}) + \theta(FFS_{i2} - FFS_1) + (\mu_i - \mu_i) + (\varepsilon_{i2} - \varepsilon_{i1})$$

Or more simply:

$$\Delta DQ_i = \gamma(\Delta FAFH_i) + \theta(\Delta FFS_i) + \Delta \varepsilon_i \tag{2}$$

Equation (2) is a first-difference model, which is equivalent to a fixed-effects model when there are only two observations per person. Because the 2 days of dietary intake in the data are collected 7-10 days apart, it is reasonable to assume that the majority of these relevant, unobservable factors are fixed during the survey period.[7] Thus, even though data are not available on all relevant, unobservable factors, such as food preferences, parental time constraints, and access to food outlets, this approach controls for factors that remain fixed over the survey period because they simply fall out of equation 2 when estimating first differences.

While the first-difference model removes the bias from the estimates of ã and è from time-invariant unobserved factors, there may still be some bias from unobserved time-varying factors. To help control for time-varying unobserved factors, such as daily variations in parental time constraints, we also estimate for the effects of changing meal patterns, such as whether an individual skipped breakfast on one of the days, whether the number of snacks consumed changed, and whether the recall day was on a weekday or weekend.

$$\Delta DQ_i = \gamma(\Delta FAFH_i) + \theta(\Delta FFS_i) + \sum_{j=1}^{4} \phi_j(\Delta MEAL_{ij}) + \delta(weekend_i) + \Delta \varepsilon_i \tag{3}$$

Equation (3) is used to estimate the effects on diet quality of obtaining one additional meal from FAFH (y) and one additional meal from FFS (θ). The effects of eating occasions ($\ddot{o}_j$) are indexed by j (for example, breakfast, lunch, dinner, or snack).[8] Equation (3) estimates total energy consumed in a day and the total HEI-2005 score for all children, and then separately for elementary school children (ages 6-12) and older children (ages 13-18).

As discussed previously, it is possible that some of the negative effects of FAFH could be attributable to an increase in consumption of CSBs, which offer little in the form of nutrition other than calories. To help separate the effect of CSBs from FAFH and FFS, we add the change in consumption of CSBs (measured in units of 100 grams, or approximately 3.5 ounces):

$$\Delta DQ_i = \gamma(\Delta FAFH_i) + \theta(\Delta FFS_i) + \sum_{j=1}^{4} \phi_j(\Delta MEAL_{ij}) + \lambda(\Delta CSB_i)$$
$$+\delta(\Delta weekend_i) + \Delta \varepsilon_i \tag{4}$$

In equation (4), y again estimates the effect of a meal from FAFH, and estimates the effect of a meal from FFS; however, these effects now hold the consumption of CSBs constant. Thus, the effect for FAFH and FFS in equation (4) is net of the change in consumption of CSBs. A comparison of the estimates from (4) with those from (3) reveals the degree to which consumption of CSBs accounts for the total effects of FAFH and FFS. Dependent variables include total daily calories, total HEI score, and specific HEI components—total fruit, whole fruit, whole grain, milk, all vegetables, dark-green/orange vegetables, share of calories from saturated fat, and extra calories.

Estimates by Survey to Test for Differences Over Time

After equation (4) is estimated with the pooled data for all children and for both age groups, it is estimated separately for the 1994-96 and 2003-04 samples to test whether the effect of eating out on various measures of diet quality changed over time. Both restaurant and school food environments underwent changes in recent years, possibly modifying the effect that consumption of food obtained from these sources has on individual diet quality. In the case of restaurants, many establishments voluntarily began to provide nutritional information for menu items, as well as to modify their menu offerings to include more healthful options. Greater media exposure of the potential negative effects of FAFH may have swayed some consumers to alter their food choices when dining out.

In the case of schools, a number of legislative acts and policy changes since 1994 may have spurred changes in the quality of FFS. The 1994 Healthy Meals for Healthy Americans Act effected changes in nutrition standards for school meals by placing a priority on limiting fat and saturated fat (see Ralston et al., 2008, for policies affecting the National School Lunch Program). While the average fat content of school meals has declined since the 1990s (Gordon et al., 2007), USDA breakfasts and lunches in many schools still do not meet nutrition standards for fat and saturated fat (Crepinsek et al., 2009). Schools are encouraged, but not required, to serve more dark-green and orange vegetables, more whole grains, and less sodium. In 2004-05, few schools served the recommended amounts of these food groups. Also, virtually no schools served meals that met the sodium limits suggested by the 2005 *Dietary Guidelines for Americans*. Not surprisingly, the American food supply and the average American diet are also excessively high in sodium (Carlson et al., 2007; Guenther et al., 2008).

In addition to changes in USDA school meals, changes in the availability of competitive foods may affect the relationship between FFS and diet quality. In recent years, more States and school districts have taken actions to limit or ban the availability of low-nutrient, energy-dense competitive foods in schools (Trust for America's Health, 2009). Despite these efforts, findings in the School Nutrition Dietary Assessment Study (SNDA) III reveal that in 2004-05, such foods were still widely available in American schools, particularly in middle and high schools (Fox et al., 2009).

EFFECTS OF FAFH, FFS, AND CSB ON DIET QUALITY

Without Controlling for the Effect of Caloric Sweetened Beverages, Each Meal Away from Home Adds 106 Calories to Total Daily Energy Intake; Meals from School Add Half as Much

Our findings suggest that, even after controlling for the unobserved characteristics affecting both FAFH consumption and diet quality, FAFH has an adverse impact on various measures of children's diet quality. Because the analysis controls for each meal consumed, the coefficients on FAFH and FFS estimate the difference between a meal obtained from either source (FAFH or FFS) and a meal obtained from home. Based on estimates obtained using equation (3) (first column of results for each sample), for all children, each meal away from home is estimated to add 106 calories to the total daily calories that would have been obtained if all meals were obtained from home (table 5). FFS is estimated to add 55 calories to total daily intake. The estimated effects vary between the two age groups. Among children ages 6-12, each FAFH meal adds 65 calories to the total daily intake, while each FFS meal has no significant effect. Among older children, FAFH and FFS have similar effects on total calories—each adds about 145 more calories to total daily intake than does a lunch from home. However, when testing for differences between the effect of FAFH and the effect of FFS on total daily calories, we find no significant difference between the two food sources for either age group.

In terms of diet quality, we find that FAFH has a significant and negative effect on HEI-2005 scores as well. Each FAFH meal is estimated to decrease HEI scores by 2.6 points for all children (about 5 percent of the average HEI score of 48.66), 2.8 points for children ages 6-12, and 2.5 points for children ages 13-18. The effect of FFS on HEI varies by children's age. While each FFS meal is found to have no significant net effect on HEI for younger children, each meal from school is estimated to significantly decrease diet quality by 1.6 points for children ages 13-18. This likely reflects the trend toward less healthful food environments in middle and high schools than in elementary schools. However, it is important to note that even if the negative effects of FAFH or FFS on diet quality were removed, the expected HEI score would still only reach 50 out of a possible 100 points. This highlights the fact that issues of poor diet quality relative to dietary recommendations are pervasive in our food choices and unlikely to improve solely by adjusting FAFH and FFS policies.

Controlling for Intake of Caloric Sweetened Beverages Lowers FAFH's Estimated Effect on Calories

After controlling for the change in the amount of caloric sweetened beverages consumed (equation 4), the analysis finds that at least some of the negative effect of FAFH is tied to the consumption of these beverages (table 5, second column of results for each sample). For all children, when the change in the amount of CSBs consumed is added to the regression, the estimate of the effect of FAFH meals drops from 106 to 65 calories added per day but the difference between FAFH and FFS remains insignificant. Each 100 grams of CSBs is estimated to increase daily caloric intake by 37 calories. (For context, a 12-ounce can of soda or other CSB weighs roughly 355 grams,[9] with the number of calories per 100 grams varying across beverage type: 100 grams of nondiet cola contain approximately 40 calories, 100 grams of fruit punch contain 50 calories, and 100 grams of a sports drink contain 20 calories.) Estimates suggest that each calorie consumed from CSBs increases daily caloric intake, in general, on a one-to-one basis. The average child in this sample consumes about 560 grams of CSBs per day (see table 3), which equates to roughly 185 extra calories per day.

When the sample is split into two age categories, the standard errors increase and the estimates become less precise. As such, the coefficients on FAFH and FFS after controlling for CSB consumption may overlap with those generated without controlling for CSB intake. However, the general pattern is the same as that observed in the full sample. For children ages 6-12, neither FAFH nor FFS has a significant effect on daily caloric intake after accounting for consumption of CSBs, and CSBs are estimated to add 39 calories to intake (per 100 grams). For older children (ages 13-18), the effect on intake of all FAFH is reduced (107 calories per meal) after accounting for CSB consumption (100 grams of CSB increase intake by 35 calories), and the net effect of food from school remains at 145 calories.

Even After Controlling for CSB Consumption, FAFH Adversely Affects HEI-2005 Total Scores

Controlling for CSB consumption reduces the effect of FAFH and FFS on calories but not the effect of FAFH on total HEI scores. After controlling for CSBs, each FAFH meal reduces the total HEI-2005 score by just over 2 points for all children (see table 5), which is roughly 4 percent of the mean score. Point estimates are similar for both age groups. FFS has no significant effect on the HEI score for all children and for children ages 6-12. However, each FFS meal reduces the total HEI-2005 score for older children (ages 13-18) by 1.6 points. Again, this may be due to greater access to competitive and a la carte foods for students in middle and high schools.

On average, every 100 grams of CSBs reduces HEI scores for all children by 0.5 points (1.1 percent); the equivalent of a 12-ounce soda is estimated to reduce scores by 1.8 points, or 3.5 percent from the mean score. The effects of CSBs also differ by age group, with a larger negative effect among younger children (0.74 points per 100 grams; 2.5 points per 12 ounces) than among older children (0.4 points per 100 grams; 1.4 points per 12 ounces). Because CSB consumption is found to have a significant effect on calorie intake and diet quality for both age groups, the analysis controls for CSB consumption in all remaining regressions.

FAFH Lowers Children's Diet Quality by Reducing Intake of Food Groups for which Consumption is Encouraged, While Increasing Intake of Those That Should be Consumed in Moderation

Analysis of the HEI component density scores shows that FAFH negatively affects children's diet quality by reducing dietary density, or share of total calories, of the food groups that are encouraged—fruit, whole fruit, whole grains, all vegetables, and dark-green vegetables (table 6). At the same time, FAFH increases the share of calories from components that are already consumed in excess—saturated fat, sodium, and extra calories (added sugar and solid fat). The adverse effect of FAFH on HEI component scores, except for those on fruits and whole grains, is more pronounced among older children.

Among all children, each meal from FFS increases the density of milk in the diet. Among younger children, FFS also reduces the density of sodium in the diet. Among older children, who typically face a less healthful food environment in schools, each FFS meal has a significant and adverse effect on several components of diet quality: it lowers the dietary density of total fruit, whole grains, and dark-green vegetables and increases the density of saturated fat and extra calories (those from added sugar and solid fat). Though the effect is less pronounced, FFS is also estimated to increase the share of calories from saturated fat among younger children.

For both groups of children, consumption of CSBs reduces the density of all healthful meal components (except all vegetables) and increases intake of extra calories. As stated earlier, CSB consumption as measured in calories has a nearly one-to-one relationship with increases in daily caloric intake. These findings suggest that CSBs decrease HEI component measures by adding calories that contain little else besides added sugar. Thus, the negative effects of FAFH on the diet quality of children may be mitigated by replacing the standard beverage in restaurant meals, usually some sort of soft drink, with a more healthful alternative, such as water or low-fat milk

Table 5. Effects of Meals Consumed from FAFH and FFS on Daily Energy Intake and HEI-2005 Scores of Children Ages 6-18

Energy	All children ages 6-18		Ages 6-12		Ages 13-18	
FAFH meal	106.417***	64.915***	64.738**	17.234	144.388***	107.499***
	(20.974)	(18.693)	(25.416)	(21.180)	(31.412)	(30.687)
FFS meal	54.711*	76.615**	10.637	44.804	146.435***	144.819***
	(30.009)	(29.627)	(40.484)	(42.765)	(48.356)	(46.607)
100 grams of CSB		37.026***		39.216***		34.742***
		(2.728)		(5.568)		(4.140)
Observations	5285	5285	2677	2677	2608	2608
R-squared	0.11	0.16	0.09	0.14	0.13	0.18
Gap between FFS and FAFH	51.705	-11.699	54.102	-27.570	-2.046	-37.321
HEI						
FAFH meal	-2.608***	-2.019***	-2.810***	-1.917***	-2.479***	-2.039***
	(0.362)	(0.355)	(0.429)	(0.431)	(0.432)	(0.417)
FFS meal	-0.205	-0.515	0.403	-0.239	-1.601***	-1.581**
	(0.465)	(0.498)	(0.784)	(0.780)	(0.585)	(0.600)
100 grams of CSB		-0.525***		-0.737***		-0.415***
		(0.044)		(0.081)		(0.041)
Observations	5285	5285	2677	2677	2608	2608
R-squared	0.05	0.09	0.05	0.10	0.05	0.09
Gap between FFS and FAFH	-2.403***	-1.504**	-3.213***	-1.677*	-0.878	-0.457

FAFH = food away from home: FFS = food from school (includes all foods obtained at school). CSB = caloric sweetened beverages. Standard errors in parentheses; *** significant at 1 percent, ** significant at 5 percent, * significant at 10 percent; additional controls include whether the respondent ate breakfast, lunch, dinner, or a snack each day and whether the recall day was on a weekend; survey weights and complex design incorporated using svy command in STATA 10.1. HEI = Healthy Eating Index.

Source: USDA, Economic Research Service.

Among Both Younger and Older Children, There Have Been no Significant Changes in the Effects of FAFH or FFS on Calorie Intake or Diet Quality Over Time

Across time periods (1994-96 and 2003-04), there are few statistically significant changes in the effects of FAFH, FFS, and CSB intake for younger children (tables 7 and 8). While in many cases, the point estimates differ across the two periods, small sample sizes and subsequent large standard errors lead to statistically insignificant differences. The only notable changes between the two time periods are in the effect of CSB consumption on diet quality— between 1994-96 and 2003-04, the adverse effect of CSBs on milk intake declined and the effect on extra calories was mixed. For younger children, the effect of CSBs grew between 1994-96 and 2003-04. For older children, the effect decreased. While statistically significant, the estimated effects were quite small.[10]

DISCUSSION AND POLICY IMPLICATIONS

This study's findings support the contention that increased consumption of FAFH is a contributing factor in the current epidemic of childhood obesity. Compared with foods prepared at home, FAFH is associated with increased caloric intake and lower diet quality, especially among older children. These effects are found after employing a methodology that controls for underlying personal characteristics and circumstances, such as access to food outlets, which might affect intake. This strengthens the argument that there is a causal relationship between FAFH and increased caloric consumption and decreased dietary quality. These findings also support policy and educational efforts designed to help children and their parents make more informed food and beverage choices when eating away from home.

One of the most common choices when eating away from home is consumption of caloric sweetened beverages. Our analysis finds that much, but not all, of the adverse dietary effect of FAFH is driven by its association with increased consumption of CSBs. The effect of CSB consumption on caloric intake is particularly striking: each calorie consumed from CSBs adds almost 1 additional calorie to overall daily intake. CSB consumption also lowers diet quality, reducing the overall share of calories of healthful foods, such as fruits, whole grains, and milk. The addition of calories lacking in any food components other than added sugar will tend to decrease density. CSBs may also displace consumption of more healthful beverages, such as milk and fruit juice, which may explain reductions in the densities of milk and total fruit components in the diets of children. Efforts to reduce children's consumption of CSBs include restrictions on the availability of these beverages at schools and other locations primarily serving children, such as community recreation centers (IOM, 2009), and nutrition education efforts. Some fast food and other restaurants have begun offering milk or juice as beverages with children's meals. Taxes on CSBs have also been proposed as a strategy for limiting general consumption (Brownell and Frieden, 2009; Chaloupka et al., 2009; IOM, 2005). The relative effectiveness of these approaches deserves further investigation.

Findings on the nutritional effects of food obtained at school reveal striking differences by age group. Among younger children, FFS does not add to caloric intake or decrease diet quality. Among older children, the adverse effects of FFS on the diets are similar to those of other FAFH, in that each adds similar amounts of calories to the daily diet. This likely reflects the prevalence of low-nutrient, high-energy competitive foods available as snacks in middle and high schools (Fox et al., 2009). These are foods sold outside the regular school lunch and breakfast program, which follow guidelines set by USDA. FFS has a somewhat less negative effect than other FAFH on overall diet quality for this age group.

Although these findings do not support arguments that food obtained from school contributes to the obesity epidemic, neither does it show that school food leads to improvement in the many areas in which the diets of American children are lacking. Overall, American children eat too few fruits, dark- green and orange vegetables, and whole grains. Given the considerable Federal investment in school meal programs, it is reasonable to investigate how school food can do more to address these shortfalls. The recent IOM report *School Meals: Building Blocks for Healthy Children* proposes new Federal meal standards that would require meals to serve more of these underconsumed dietary components. USDA Secretary Thomas Vilsack has announced his intention to transform these recommendations into updated Federal regulations (USDA, 2009); such actions may have positive impacts on FFS quality. USDA has legislative authority to regulate foods sold as part of the reimbursable meal, so any updates to the current Federal regulations will not apply to many of the other foods that compete for students' attention, such as the a la carte items also sold in school cafeterias.

Table 6. Effects of meals consumed from FAFH and FFS on HEI component densities of children ages 6-18

	Total fruit			Whole fruit			Whole grains		
	All children ages 6-18	Ages 6-12	Ages 13-18	All children ages 6-18	Ages 6-12	Ages 13-18	All children ages 6-18	Ages 6-12	Ages 13-18
FAFH meal	-0.051*** (0.012)	-0.063*** (0.021)	-0.041** (0.019)	-0.045*** (0.011)	-0.045** (0.022)	-0.040*** (0.013)	-0.041*** (0.011)	-0.059*** (0.019)	-0.027* (0.014)
FFS meal	-0.022 (0.027)	0.004 (0.036)	-0.079** (0.034)	-0.015 (0.021)	-0.035 (0.029)	-0.000 (0.017)	-0.069** (0.030)	-0.060 (0.039)	-0.066** (0.026)
100 grams of caloric sweetened beverage	-0.021*** (0.002)	-0.025*** (0.004)	-0.018*** (0.003)	-0.009*** (0.001)	-0.015*** (0.002)	-0.006*** (0.002)	-0.002* (0.001)	-0.002 (0.003)	-0.003 (0.002)
R-squared Gap between FFS and FAFH	0.04 - 0.029	0.05 - 0.067	0.03 0.038	0.02 - 0.030	0.03 - 0.010	0.01 - 0.040	0.01 0.028	0.02 0.001	0.02 0.039

	Dairy			All vegetables			Dark-green vegetables		
	All children ages 6-18	Ages 6-12	Ages 13-18	All children ages 6-18	Ages 6-12	Ages 13-18	All children ages 6-18	Ages 6-12	Ages 13-18
FAFH meal	0.004 (0.022)	-0.010 (0.028)	0.010 (0.024)	-0.065*** (0.018)	-0.040* (0.023)	-0.082*** (0.025)	-0.026*** (0.003)	-0.018*** (0.005)	-0.032*** (0.004)
FFS meal	0.203*** (0.027)	0.221*** (0.036)	0.173*** (0.040)	0.023 (0.023)	-0.000 (0.021)	0.049 (0.042)	-0.011* (0.006)	-0.006 (0.006)	-0.023*** (0.008)

	Dairy			All vegetables			Dark-green vegetables		
	All children ages 6-18	Ages 6-12	Ages 13-18	All children ages 6-18	Ages 6-12	Ages 13-18	All children ages 6-18	Ages 6-12	Ages 13-18
FFS meal	0.203*** (0.027)	0.221*** (0.036)	0.173*** (0.040)	0.023 (0.023)	-0.000 (0.021)	0.049 (0.042)	-0.011* (0.006)	-0.006 (0.006)	-0.023*** (0.008)
100 grams of CSB	-0.025*** (0.002)	-0.024*** (0.005)	-0.027*** (0.003)	-0.004* (0.002)	-0.009*** (0.003)	-0.001 (0.003)	-0.001* (0.001)	-0.001 (0.001)	-0.001 (0.001)
R-squared	0.10	0.11	0.09	0.02	0.02	0.03	0.02	0.01	0.03
Gap between FFS and FAFH	-0.200***	-0.232***	-0.163***	-0.088***	-0.039	-0.130***	-0.0146**	-0.012	-0.009
FAFH meal	0.466*** (0.103)	0.456*** (0.147)	0.491*** (0.151)	-47.773*** (15.712)	-39.557** (17.175)	-50.304** (23.588)	1.637*** (0.270)	1.407*** (0.305)	1.752*** (0.371)
FFS meal	0.514*** (0.140)	0.417** (0.188)	0.737*** (0.214)	-28.508* (16.547)	-56.963*** (19.875)	21.270 (32.445)	0.835** (0.340)	0.800 (0.512)	1.293*** (0.430)
100 grams of CSB	-0.113*** (0.013)	-0.098*** (0.018)	-0.124*** (0.017)	-13.027*** (1.653)	-13.363*** (2.569)	-13.133*** (2.097)	0.803*** (0.045)	0.938*** (0.091)	0.731 (0.042)
R-squared	0.04	0.03	0.06	0.04	0.03	0.05	0.21	0.20	0.22
Gap between FFS and FAFH	-0.048	0.040	0.246	-19.265	17.405	-71.574*	0.802*	0.607	0.459

FAFH = food away from home: FFS = food from school (includes all foods obtained at school): N=5,825. CSB = caloric sweetened beverages. Standard errors in parentheses; *** significant at 1 percent; ** significant at 5 percent; * significant at 10 percent; additional controls include whether the respondent ate breakfast, lunch, dinner, or a snack each day and whether the recall day was on a weekend; survey weights and complex design incorporated using svy command in Stata 10.1. HEI = Healthy Eating Index.

Source: USDA, Economic Research Service.

Table 7. Effects of FAFH and FFS on Total Calories, HEI-2005, and Component Densities of Children Ages 6 to 12

	Energy		Total HEI score		Total fruit			Whole fruit		
	1994-96	2003-04	1994-96	2003-04	1994-96	2003-04		1994-96	2003-04	
FAFH meal	3.106	38.909	-1.868***	-1.763**	-0.076***	-0.041		-0.050**	-0.031	
	(31.881)	(22.563)	(0.547)	(0.679)	(0.025)	(0.036)		(0.025)	(0.037)	
FFS meal	41.238	49.427	0.152	-0.623	0.015	-0.009		0.012	-0.077	
	(33.491)	(75.096)	(0.654)	(1.466)	(0.041)	(0.059)		(0.030)	(0.046)	
100 grams of CSB	38.369***	42.441***	-0.775***	-0.683***	-0.037***	-0.019***	++	-0.020***	-0.012***	+
	(5.347)	(7.583)	(0.077)	(0.120)	(0.005)	(0.005)		(0.004)	(0.003)	
R-squared	0.19	0.13	0.11	0.11	0.07	0.04		0.05	0.04	
Gap between FFS and FAFH	-38.132	-10.51777	-2.020**	-1.1396	-0.091**	-0.0322		-0.062**	0.0462	

	Whole grains		Dairy		All vegetables		Dark-green vegetables		
	1994-96	2003-04	1994-96	2003-04	1994-96	2003-04	1994-96	2003-04	
FAFH meal	-0.021	-0.088** +	0.005	-0.028	-0.024	-0.057	-0.015**	-0.021**	
	(0.021)	(0.033)	(0.030)	(0.055)	(0.020)	(0.041)	(0.007)	(0.009)	
FFS meal	-0.023	-0.093	0.216***	0.222***	-0.012	0.018	-0.015	0.003	
	(0.025)	(0.077)	(0.033)	(0.066)	(0.023)	(0.034)	(0.010)	(0.007)	
100 grams of CSB	-0.009**	0.006 ++	-0.042***	-0.012** +++	-0.005	-0.010**	-0.001	-0.000	
	(0.004)	(0.005)	(0.006)	(0.005)	(0.004)	(0.005)	(0.001)	(0.001)	
R-squared	0.01	0.04	0.14	0.10	0.01	0.04	0.01	0.02	
Gap between FFS and FAFH	0.002	0.005 +	-0.163***	-0.088***	-0.012	-0.075	0.000	-0.025	

	Percent saturated fat		Sodium		Extra calories		
	1994-96	2003-04	1994-96	2003-04	1994-96	2003-04	
FAFH meal	0.400**	0.550**	-46.007**	-29.850	1.853***	0.796 +	
	(0.193)	(0.216)	(23.575)	(23.754)	(0.365)	(0.499)	
FFS meal	0.347*	0.456	-79.741**	-38.321*	0.628	0.987	
	(0.183)	(0.325)	(35.211)	(21.720)	(0.478)	(0.920)	
100 grams of CSB	-0.138***	-0.079**	-12.108***	-14.688***	0.957***	0.917***	
	(0.026)	(0.029)	(4.230)	(3.189)	(0.070)	(0.132)	
R-squared	0.04	0.03	0.03	0.04	0.17	0.23	
Gap between FFS and FAFH	0.054	0.094	33.735	8.472	1.225**	-0.191 +	

FAFH = food away from home: FFS = food from school (includes all foods obtained at school); N=1,608. CSB = caloric sweetened beverages. HEI = Healthy Eating Index. Standard errors in parentheses; *** significant at 1 percent, ** significant at 5 percent, * significant at 10 percent; +++ difference between 1994-96 and 2003-04 is significant at 1 percent; ++ difference between 1994-96 is significant at 5 percent, + difference between 1994-96 is significant at 10 percent; additional controls include whether the respondent ate breakfast, lunch, dinner, or a snack each day and whether the recall day was on a weekend; survey weights and complex design incorporated using svy command in Stata 10.1.

Source: USDA, Economic Research Service.

Table 8. Effects of FAFH and FFS on Total Calories, HEI-2005, and Component Densities of Children Ages 13-18

	Energy		Total HEI score		Total fruit		Whole fruit	
	1994-96	2003-04	1994-96	2003-04	1994-96	2003-04	1994-96	2003-04
FAFH meal	56.964	151.078***	-2.367***	-1.741**	-0.015	-0.065**	-0.017	-0.059**
	(45.367)	(43.520)	(0.453)	(0.673)	(0.029)	(0.027)	(0.019)	(0.021)
FFS meal	171.836**	119.566**	-0.499	-2.722*** +	-0.063	-0.092**	-0.009	0.006
	(75.611)	(51.902)	(0.923)	(0.714)	(0.055)	(0.036)	(0.026)	(0.020)
100 grams of CSB	36.860***	34.187***	-0.368***	-0.442***	-0.020***	-0.018***	-0.009***	-0.003 +
	(5.129)	(6.209)	(0.060)	(0.056)	(0.004)	(0.004)	(0.003)	(0.002)
R-squared	0.18	0.20	0.09	0.10	0.03	0.05	0.01	0.02
Gap between FFS and FAFH	-114.872	31.512	-1.867*	0.980	0.048	0.027	-0.008	-0.065*

	Whole grains		Dairy		All vegetables		Dark-green vegetables	
	1994-96	2003-04	1994-96	2003-04	1994-96	2003-04	1994-96	2003-04
FAFH meal	-0.027	-0.027	0.005	0.018	-0.080**	-0.077**	-0.035***	-0.028***
	(0.020)	(0.021)	(0.020)	(0.043)	(0.034)	(0.032)	(0.006)	(0.006)
FFS meal	-0.061*	-0.068	0.127***	0.220***	0.035	0.042	-0.020	-0.028***
	(0.035)	(0.039)	(0.044)	(0.069)	(0.039)	(0.067)	(0.013)	(0.009)
100 grams of CSB	-0.002	-0.004	-0.031***	-0.024***	-0.004	0.003	-0.001	-0.000
	(0.002)	(0.003)	(0.003)	(0.004)	(0.004)	(0.003)	(0.001)	(0.001)
R-squared	0.02	0.04	0.12	0.09	0.03	0.04	0.03	0.02
Gap between FFS and FAFH	0.034	0.041	-0.122**	-0.203***	-0.115**	-0.118*	-0.015	0.000

	Percent saturated fat		Sodium		Extra calories			
	1994-96	2003-04	1994-96	2003-04	1994-96	2003-04		
FAFH meal	0.464***	0.503*	-65.874**	-36.513	2.399***	1.043* +		
	(0.157)	(0.262)	(25.961)	(39.543)	(0.477)	(0.506)		
FFS meal	0.697**	0.780***	21.843	14.003	0.620	2.077*** +		
	(0.308)	(0.264)	(35.301)	(53.752)	(0.776)	(0.316)		
100 grams of CSB	-0.125***	-0.119***	-14.699***	-11.085***	0.751***	0.690***		
	(0.021)	(0.026)	(2.316)	(3.249)	(0.058)	(0.057)		
R-squared	0.06	0.06	0.05	0.05	0.24	0.21		

FAFH = food away from home: FFS = food from school (includes all foods obtained at school): N=1,082. CSB = caloric sweetened beverages. HEI = Healthy Eating Index. Standard errors in parentheses; *** significant at 1 percent, ** significant at 5 percent, * significant at 10 percent; + indicates the difference between the two time periods is significant at 10 percent; additional controls include whether the respondent ate breakfast, lunch, dinner, or a snack each day and whether the recall day was on a weekend; survey weights and complex design incorporated using svy command in Stata 10.1.

Source: USDA, Economic Research Service.

In general, our findings suggest that consumption of food prepared outside the home has particularly negative effects on the diets of older children and adolescents. Foods available to these children from both commercial and school sources add calories and decrease diet quality. Moreover, older children eat more nonhome foods: on average they eat 50 percent more FAFH meals and twice as many FAFH snacks as younger children. Older children and adolescents typically have more freedom, more time with peers, more spending money of their own, and, therefore, more opportunities to make their own food choices, at school and elsewhere, than younger children. Unfortunately, older children are opting for less healthful and nutritious foods.

Several of the most widely discussed proposals for improving children's diets, such as improving the nutritional quality of "children's meals" sold at fast food and other restaurants or restricting food advertising for television programs watched by children under age 12, are targeted to younger children and would have little or no effect on older children and adolescents. More investigation of appropriate and effective strategies targeting this older age group seems warranted. Devising such strategies, however, may be a challenge; during adolescence, peer influences on behavior, including food choice, are strong and may trump nutrition advice (Stang and Story, 2005). Nevertheless, given the importance of this stage to an individual's growth, development, and formation of longer term habits (Kelder et al., 1994), it merits more consideration.

A broad range of public and private groups have expressed a strong interest in improving children's diets. Many of the proposed policy and educational efforts aimed at improving child nutrition and preventing obesity focus on food obtained from fast food and other restaurant and commercial sources, foods obtained at school, and caloric sweetened beverages. Findings in this study point to the importance of these areas of policy focus and provide insights that can help inform selection and design of nutrition policies and strategies.

REFERENCES

Behrman, Jere R. & Anil Deolalikar. B. (1990). "The Intrahousehold Demand for Nutrients in Rural South India: Individual Estimates, Fixed Effects, and Permanent Income," *The Journal of Human Resources*, Vol, *25(4)*, 665-96.

Bleich, S. N., Wang, Y. C. Wang, Y. & Gortmaker. S. L. (2009). "Increasing Consumption of Sugar-Sweetened Beverages Among U.S. Adults: 1988-1994 to 1999-2004," *American Journal of Clinical Nutrition*, Vol, *89(1)*, 372-38 1.

Block, Jason P., Richard A. Scribner, & Karen B. DeSalvo. (2004). "Fast Food, Race/Ethnicity, and Income: A Geographic Analysis," *American Journal of Preventive Medicine*, Vol, *27(3),* 211-217.

Bowman, Shanthy A., Steven L. Gortmaker, Cara B. Ebbeling, Mark A. Pereira, & David S. Ludwig. (2004a). "Effects of Fast-Food Consumption on Energy Intake and Diet Quality Among Children in a National Household Survey," *Pediatrics*, Vol, *113(1),* 112-118.

Bowman, S. A., Friday, J. E. & Moshfegh. A. (2008). *MyPyramid Equivalents Database, 2 .0 for USDA Survey Foods*, 2003-2004, U.S. Department of Agriculture, Agricultural Research Service, Food Surveys Research Group, www.ars.usda.gov/ba/bhnrc/fsrg/

Bowman, Shanthy A., & Bryan T. Vinyard. (2004b). "Fast Food Consumption of U.S. Adults: Impact on Energy and Nutrient Intakes and Overweight Status," *Journal of the American College of Nutrition*, Vol, *23(2),* 163-168.

Briefel, Ronette, Mary Kay Crepinsek, Charlotte Cabili, Ander Wilson, & Philip Gleason. (2009). "School Food Environments and Practices Affect Dietary Behaviors of U.S. Public School Children," *Journal of American Dietetic Association*, Supplement 1, Vol, *109(2),* S91-S 107

Brownell, K. D., & Frieden. T. R. (2009). "Ounces of Prevention—The Public Policy Case for Taxes on Sugared Beverages, *New England Journal of Medicine, 360(18),* 1805-1808.

Burdette, Hillary L., & Robert C. Whitaker. (2004). "Neighborhood Playgrounds, Fast Food Restaurants and Crime: Relationships to Overweight in Low-Income Preschool Children," *Preventive Medicine*, Vol, *38,* 57-63.

Carlson, Andrea, Mark Lino, WenYen Juan, Kenneth Hanson, & Peter Basiotis. (2007). *Thrifty Food Plan, 2006*, CNPP-19, U.S. Department of Agriculture, Center for Nutrition Policy and Promotion.

Centers for Disease Control and Prevention (CDC), Division of Adolescent & School Health. (2007). *School Health Policies and Programs Study, 2006: Changes Between 2000 and 2006*, www.cdc.gov/HealthyYouth/ shpps/2006/factsheets/pdf/FS_Trends_SHPPS2006.pdf

Centers for Disease Control & Prevention (CDC). (2009). *Overweight and Obesity: Obesity Trends—NHANES Surveys (1976-1980 and 2003-2006)*, www.cdc.gov/nccdphp/dnpa/obesity

Centers for Disease Control and Prevention (CDC), Division of Nutrition & Physical Activity. (2006). *Research to Practices Series No. 3: Does*

Drinking Beverages with Added Sugars Increase the Risk of Overweight?
www.cdc.gov/nccdphp/dnpa/nutrition

Chaloupka, F. J., Powell, L. M. & Chriqui. J. F. (2009). *Sugar-Sweetened Beverage Taxes and Public Health*, Research Brief, Robert Wood Johnson Foundation and School of Public Health, University of Minnesota, July.

Condon, Elizabeth M., Mary Kay Crepinsek, & Mary Kay Fox. (2009). "School Meals: Types of Foods Offered to and Consumed by Children at Lunch and Breakfast," *Journal of the American Dietetic Association*, Vol, *109*, S67-S78.

Crepinsek, Mary Kay, Anne R. Gordon, Patricia M. McKinney, Elizabeth M. Condon, & Ander Wilson. (2009). "Meals Offered and Served in U.S. Public Schools: Do They Meet Nutrient Standards?" *Journal of the American Dietetic Association*, Vol *109*, S31-S43.

Currie, Janet, Stefano DellaVigna, Enrico Moretti, & Vikram Pathania. (2009). "The Effect of Fast Food Restaurants on Obesity and Weight Gain," NBER Working Paper Series, Working Paper 14721, www.nber.org/papers/w 14721

Ebbeling, Cara B., Kelly B. Sinclair, Mark A. Pereira, Erica Garcia-Lago, Henry A. Feldman, & David S. Ludwig. (2004). "Compensation for Energy Intake From Fast Food Among Overweight and Lean Adolescents," *Journal of the American Medical Association*, 29 1(23), 2828-2833.

Finkelstein, Daniel M., Elaine L. Hill, & Robert C. Whitaker. (2008). "School Food Environments and Policies in U.S. Public Schools," *Pediatrics*, Vol, 122(1), e251-e259.

Food Research and Action Center (FRAC). (2009). *School Breakfast Scorecard: School Year 2008-2009*, www.frac.org/pdf/breakfast09.pdf

Fox, Mary Kay, Anne Gordon, Renee Nogales, & Ander Wilson. (2009). "Availability and Consumption of Competitive Foods in U.S. Public Schools," *Journal of the American Dietetic Association*, Vol, *109*, S57-S66.

French, S. A., Story, M. Neumark-Sztainer, D. Fulkerson, J. A. & Hannan. P. (2001). "Fast Food Restaurant Use Among Adolescents: Associations With Nutrient Intake, Food Choices and Behavioral and Psychosocial Variables," *International Journal of Obesity*, Vol. *25*, 1823-1833.

Friday, J. E. & Bowman. S. A. (2006). MyPyramid Equivalents Database for USDA Survey Food Codes, 1994-2002 Version 1.0. U.S. Departmentof Agriculture, Agricultural Research Service, Community Nutrition Research Group, www.ars.usda.gov/ba/bhnrc/fsrg/

Fungwe, Thomas, Patricia Guenther, Wen Yen Juan, Hazel Hiza, & Mark Lino. (2009). *The Quality of Children's Diets in 2003-2004 as Measured by the Healthy Eating Index-2005*, Nutrition Insight 43, U.S. Department of Agriculture, Center for Nutrition Policy and Promotion.

Gable, Sara, Jo Britt-Rankin, & Jennifer L. Krull. (2008). *Ecological Predictors and Developmental Outcomes of Persistent Childhood Overweight*, Contractor and Cooperator Report No. 42, U.S. Department of Agriculture, Economic Research Service.

Gillis, Linda J. & Oded Bar-Or. (2003). "Food Away from Home, Sugar-Sweetened Drink Consumption and Juvenile Obesity," *Journal of the American College of Nutrition*, Vol, *22(6)*, 539-545.

Gordon, A., Mary Kay Fox, Melissa Clark, Rénee Nogales, Elizabeth Condon, Philip Gleason, & Ankur Sarin. (2007). *School Nutrition Dietary Assessment Study-III: Vol. II: Student Participation and Dietary Intakes*, U.S. Department of Agriculture, Food and Nutrition Service, Office of Research, Nutrition and Analysis.

Guenther, Patricia M., Jill Reedy, & Susan M. Krebs-Smith. (2008). "Development and Evaluation of the Healthy Eating Index-2005," *Journal of the American Dietetic Association*, Vol, *108(11)*, 1896-1901.

Guenther, Patricia, Wen Yen Juan, Mark Lino, Hazel Hiza, Thomas Fungwe, *and* Richard Lucas. (2009). *Diet Quality of Low-Income and Higher Income Americans in 2003-2004 as Measured by the Healthy Eating Index-2005*, Nutrition Insight 42, U.S. Department of Agriculture, Center for Nutrition Policy and Promotion.

Guthrie, Joanne F., Biing-Hwan Lin, & Elizabeth Frazao. (2002). "Role of Food Prepared Away from Home in the American Diet, 1977-78 Versus 1994-96: Changes and Consequences," *Journal of Nutrition Education and Behavior*, Vol. *34(3)*, 140-150.

Hersch, Joni, & Leslie S. Stratton. (1997)."Housework, Fixed Effects, and Wages of Married Workers," *The Journal of Human Resources, 32(2)*, 285-3 07.

Institute of Medicine, Committee on Nutrition Standards for National School Lunch & Breakfast Programs (IOM). (2009). *School Meals: Building Blocks for Healthy Children*, Washington, DC: National Academies Press.

Institute of Medicine, Committee on Prevention of Obesity in Children & Youth (IOM). (2005). *Preventing Childhood Obesity: Health in the Balance*, J.P. Koplan, C.T. Liverman, and V.I. Kraak (eds.). Washington, DC: National Academies Press.

Kelder, S. H., Perry, C. L. Klepp, K. I. & Lytle. L. L. (1994). "Longitudinal Tracking of Adolescent Smoking, Physical Activity, and Food Choice Behaviors," *American Journal of Public Health*, Vol, *84(7)*, 1121-1126.

Lin, Biing-Hwan, Joanne Guthrie, & Elizabeth Frazao. (2001). "American Children's Diets Not Making the Grade," *FoodReview*, Vol. *24 (2)*, 8-17.

Ludwig David, K. Peterson, & S. Gortmaker. (2001). "Relation Between Consumption of Sugar-Sweetened Drinks and Childhood Obesity: A Prospective, Observational Analysis," *The Lancet*, Vol, *357(9255)*, 505-508.

Malik, V. S., Schulze, M. B. & Hu. F. B. (2006). "Intake of Sugar-Sweetened Beverages and Weight Gain: A Systematic Review," *American Journal of Clinical Nutrition*, Vol, *84(2)*, 274-288.

Mancino, Lisa, Jessica Todd, & Biing-Hwan Lin. (2009). "Separating What We Eat From Where: Measuring the Effect of Food Away From Home on Diet Quality," *Food Policy*, Vol, *34 (6)*, 557-562.

Mattes, Richard D. (1996). "Dietary Compensation by Humans for Supplemental Energy Provided as Ethanol or Carbohydrate in Fluids," *Physiology and Behavior*, Vol. *59*, 179-187.

Newman, Constance, Joanne Guthrie, Lisa Mancino, Katherine Ralston, & Melissa Musiker. (2009). *Meeting Total Fat Requirements for School Lunches: Influence of School Policies and Characteristics*, Economic Research Report No. 87, U.S. Department of Agriculture, Economic Research Service, www.ers.usda.gov/publications/err87/

Paeratakul, S., Ferdinand, D. Champagne, C. Ryan, D. & Bray. G. (2003). "Fast-Food Consumption Among U.S. Adults and Children: Dietary and Nutrient Intake Profile," *Journal of the American Dietetic Association*, Vol, *103(10)*, 1332-1338.

Powell, Lisa M., & Yanjun Bao. (2009). "Food Prices, Access to Food Outlets, and Child Weight," *Economics and Human Biology*, Vol. *7*, 64-72.

Ralston, Katherine, Constance Newman, Annette Clauson, Joanne Guthrie, & Jean Buzby. (2008). *The National School Lunch Program: Background, Trends, and Issues,* Economic Research Report No. 61, U.S. Department of Agriculture, Economic Research Service, www.ers.usda.gov/ publications/ err61/

Rosenheck, R. (2008). "Fast Food Consumption and Increased Caloric Intake: A Systematic Review of a Trajectory Towards Weight Gain and Obesity Risk," *Obesity Reviews*, Vol, *9*, 535-547.

Sebastian, Rhonda, Cecilia Wilkinson Enns, & Josephs D. Goldman. (2009). "U.S. Adolescents and MyPyramid: Associations Between Fast-Food

Consumption and Lower Likelihood of Meeting Recommendations," *Journal of the American Dietetic Association*, Vol, *109*, 226-235.

Stang J., & Story M. (eds.). (2005). *Guidelines for Adolescent Nutrition Services*, University of Minnesota, School of Public Health, Division of Epidemiology and Community Health, Center for Leadership, Education and Training in Maternal and Child Nutrition.

Sturm, R., & Datar. A. (2005). "Body Mass Index in Elementary School Children, Metropolitan Area Food Prices and Food Outlet Density," *Journal of the Royal Institute of Public Health*, Vol, *119*, 1059-1068.

Todd, Jessica, Lisa Mancino, & Biing-Hwan Lin. (2010). *The Impact of Food Away From Home on Adult Diet Quality*, Economic Research Report No. 90, U.S. Department of Agriculture, Economic Research Service, February, www.ers.usda.gov/publications/err90/

Trust for America's Health. (2009). Supplement to "F as in Fat: How Obesity Policies Are Failing in America, 2009": Obesity-Related Legislation Action in States, Update, http://healthyamericans.org/reports/ obesity2009/ StateSupplement2009.pdf

U.S. Department of Agriculture, Office of Communications. (2009). *USDA-Commissioned Report from Institute of Medicine (IOM) of the National Academies Highlights Ways To Improve National School Lunch and Breakfast Programs*, Office of Communications Release No. 0516.09.

U.S. Department of Health & Human Services (USDHHS). (2000). *Healthy People 2010: Leading Health Indicators*, www.healthypeople.gov/ Document/html/uih/uih_4.htm

U.S. Department of Health & Human Services. (2007). "The Surgeon General's Call to Action to Prevent and Decrease Overweight and Obesity," www.surgeongeneral.gov/topics/obesity adolescents .htm

U.S. Department of Health & Human Services and U.S. Department of Agriculture (USDHHS/USDA). *Dietary Guidelines for Americans*, 2005, www.health

Vartanian, L. R., Schwartz, M. B. & Brownell. K. D. (2007). "Effects of Soft Drink Consumption on Nutrition and Health: A Systematic Review and Meta-Analysis," *American Journal of Public Health*, *97(4)*, 667-675.

Wang, Y. Claire, Sara N. Bleich, & Steven L. Gortmaker. (2008). "Increasing Caloric Contribution From Sugar-Sweetened Beverages and 100% Fruit Juices Among U.S. Children and Adolescents, 1988-2004," *Pediatrics*, Vol, *121* (June), e1604 -e1614.

End Notes

[1] While many children star school by age 5, this is not always the case. Our data left some ambiguities as to whether or not a child was currently attending school. As such, we use age 6 as our lower range.

[2] Program regulations require that school lunches and breakfast provide one-third and one-quarter, respectively, of the 1989 Recommended Dietary Allowance of protein, calcium, iron, and vitamins A and C. USDA-sponsored school meals are expected to limit fat content to no more than 30 percent of the meal's calories and limit saturated fat to no more than 10 percent of calories. Schools are also encouraged to minimize sodium but are not held to a specific standard.

[3] In 2004-05, competitive foods were available in 73 percent of elementary schools, 97 percent of middle schools, and 100 percent of high schools (Fox et al., 2009). The likelihood of eating competitive foods also increases with age, with the share of students doing so rising from 29 percent in elementary school, to 44 percent in middle school, and to 55 percent in high school. At the same time, consumption of USDA school meals declines, with the share of students participating in the program dropping from 73 percent in elementary school, to 60 percent in middle school, and to 44 percent in high school.

[4] The 2005-06 NHANES intake data have been released, but the corresponding MyPyramid Equivalents Database has not.

[5] For example, a lunch obtained off campus during school hours is classified as FAFH, even if the student brought that meal back to school.

[6] For completeness, we include foods obtained at day care centers with foods obtained at schools. It is possible that some of the day care providers were located in schools, so foods available would be similar in both. These foods make up a small portion of this category—less than 4 percent of eating occasions classified as food from school contain food from day care.

[7] The fixed-effects estimator has been used extensively to remove bias from unobservable factors (see, for example, Mancino et al. (2009), who estimate the effect of FAFH on calories and HEI scores among adults; Hersch and Stratton (1997), who estimate the effect of housework time on wages; and Behrman and Deolalikar (1990), who estimate the effect of income on nutrient demand).

[8] The breakfast, lunch, and dinner variables are all dichotomous. They indicate whether an individual ate a specific meal or had at least one snack on that intake day. Thus, the differenced values used in our estimates take on values of -1. As an example, a value of -1 for breakfast would indicate an individual skipped breakfast on the first day of the recall and ate a breakfast on the second, a value of 1 would indicate he or she ate breakfast on the first day and skipped it on the second, and a value of zero would indicate no change between the 2 days The snack variable measures the change in the number of snacks eaten on the particular day.

[9] One fluid ounce is equal to 29.57 grams. Conversely, 1 gram is equal to .03381 ounces.

[10] As an example, among children ages 13-18, the estimated impact of each 12-ounce can of soda was to reduce one's daily milk density by .10 cups per 1,000 calories in 1994-96. In 2003-04, the estimated impact of a can of soda was to reduce daily milk density by .07 cups. For a 2,000 calorie-a-day diet, the difference between the two time periods is roughly equivalent to 1 tablespoon of milk.

In: Weighty Factors in Children's Food...   ISBN: 978-1-62257-917-4
Editors: C.E. Oyler and C. De Volld   © 2013 Nova Science Publishers, Inc.

Chapter 3

CHILDREN'S FOOD ENVIRONMENT STATE INDICATOR REPORT, 2011[*]

Centers for Disease Control and Prevention

The current childhood obesity epidemic is the result of many factors and may not be resolved by any single action. Rather, resolution of the childhood obesity epidemic will require concerted action across many sectors and settings such as child care facilities, communities, and schools. The 2011 Children's Food Environment State Indicator Report highlights selected behaviors, environments, and policies that affect childhood obesity through support of healthy eating. These indicators represent opportunities for action. Specific action steps and resources are detailed in the National Action Guide at http://www.cdc.gov/obesity/.

The environments to which children are exposed in their daily lives - schools, child care facilities, and their communities - can influence the healthfulness of their diets. With the high prevalence of childhood obesity in the U.S., supporting healthy food environments is a key strategy to reach the public health goals of reducing childhood obesity and improving nutrition. National and state-specific information is reported in the *Children's Food Environment State Indicator Report* for both behavioral indicators and policy and environmental indicators. Indicators selected for this report had data available for most states. However, individual states may have additional

---

[*] This is an edited, reformatted and augmented version of a Department of Health and Human Services, Centers for Disease Control and Prevention report, dated 2011.

information collected through state-wide surveys and/or policies or regulations enacted outside the monitoring period that can augment the data in this report and thus be used to further inform decision makers. On a state and local level, parents, school and child care staff, health professionals, state officials, and community members play a role in supporting policy and environmental change to ensure children and their families can choose more healthful foods.

Behavioral indicators - The 2010 Dietary Guidelines for Americans recommends limiting the consumption of added sugar among Americans.[1] The leading source of added sugar among children is sugar-sweetened drinks (also referred to as sugar drinks).[2] State progress on added-sugar in the diet is measured here by assessing consumption of sugar-sweetened or "regular" sodas among high school students. We also assess the percentage of high school students viewing 3 or more hours of television each day. An objective of *Healthy People 2020* (PA-8) is to increase the proportion of children and adolescents who do not exceed the recommended limit for screen time of no more than 2 hours a day for children 2 years and older.[3] Data for these indicators are from the 2009 national and state Youth Risk Behavior Surveys, components of CDC's Youth Risk Behavior Surveillance System (students in grades 9-12). Other behavioral indicators reflect recommendations from leading medical associations to not place televisions in children's bedrooms[4] and for children to have meals together with their family.[5] Data on those indicators are derived from the 2007 National Survey of Children's Health.

Policy and environmental indicators - The policy and environmental indicators measure components of food environments across three domains: child care facilities, schools, and the community.

> The Children's Food Environment State Indicator Report is the 4th in a series* of CDC Reports that highlight environmental and policy indicators to improve nutrition, physical activity and reduce obesity.

Data in the *Children's Food Environment State Indicator Report* can be used to:

- Monitor progress and celebrate state successes.
- Identify opportunities to improve environmental and policy approaches.

BEHAVIORAL INDICATORS

In this *Children's Food Environment State Indicator Report*, four behavioral indicators are reported.

- Percentage of high school students who drank ≥1 sugar-sweetened soda per day

Sugar drinks are the largest source of added sugar and an important contributor of calories in the diets of children in the United States.[2] Adolescent males consume, on average, around 300 calories from sugar drinks each day.[2] High consumption of sugar drinks, which have few, if any, nutrients, has been associated with obesity.[6]

- Percentage of high school students who watched television ≥3 hours per day
- Percentage of children ages 6-17 with television in their bedroom

Parents can positively impact children's sedentary activity, snacking, and exposure to advertising of unhealthy foods through rules related to TV viewing. One approach that parents can use to encourage healthy lifestyles for children at home is to not put televisions in children's bedrooms. The presence of a television in a child's bedroom has been associated with increased time spent watching television[7] and increased prevalence of obesity.[8] The link to obesity may occur through multiple mechanisms including displacement of physical activity, increased energy intake while viewing, or through greater exposure to television advertising of unhealthy foods which may affect food choices.9,10 The American Academy of Pediatrics (AAP) recommends that children should not have a television in their bedroom.[4]

- Percentage of children ages 12-17 who do not eat meals with their families most days of the week

Parents have tremendous influence on children's food behaviors.[11] Eating meals together as a family is associated with positive effects on children across many domains of life, including the development of healthy eating behaviors[12] and the maintenance of a healthy weight status.[13] Foods prepared and consumed at home may also be more nutritious than foods prepared away from home.[14]

POLICY AND ENVIRONMENTAL INDICATORS

These indicators represent three different domains or settings for improving the food environment. They correspond with recommendations by groups such as the Institute of Medicine for improvements at the local, community, or school level.[15-17] States may focus on a few or many of the indicators based on their existing capacity, partnerships, and resources.

The Child Care Facility Food Environment

According to the Federal Interagency Forum on Child and Family Statistics, 36% of all children younger than six not yet in kindergarten attend child care centers.[18] Additionally, a substantial number of children also attend commercial child care facilities operated in caregivers' homes (family child care homes).[18] However, state regulations regarding nutrition and physical activity are not consistent in their treatment of child care centers and family child care homes. Regulations that ensure both types of facilities maintain healthy food environments could help instill healthy eating habits among a large proportion of America's young children.

- State regulations restrict sugar drinks in child care centers and family child care homes
- State regulations require access to drinking water throughout the day in child care centers and family child care homes

Ensuring the availability of drinking water and limiting access to sugar drinks are ways to improve the food environment of child care facilities. Displacing sugar drinks with drinking water, a calorie-free and thirst-quenching beverage, can substantially reduce excess energy intake among children.[19] Staff can also teach the importance and healthfulness of drinking water and non-fat/low-fat milk as primary beverages.

- State regulations limit television and video time in child care centers and family child care homes

Young children are highly susceptible to the influence of advertising of unhealthy foods on television.[20] Television and video viewing during child care may also displace recreational time spent engaging in active play and physical activity.

The School Food Environment

The Institute of Medicine recommends that the sale of competitive foods in schools (food sold outside the USDA reimbursable school meal programs such as in vending machines, school stores, snack bars) be limited.[17] Schools are uniquely positioned to facilitate and reinforce healthful eating behaviors by eliminating sugar drinks and high energy density foods (foods high in calories for their volume) from the selection of foods offered on the school campus.

- Percentage of middle and high schools that offer sugar drinks as competitive foods

Although sodas are prohibited in an increasing number of schools, other sugar drinks that may not be commonly perceived as sources of added sugar and excess calories[21] may be available, such as sports drinks and fruit flavored drinks that are not 100% juice. Schools should consider adopting policies that limit access to all sugar drinks in vending machines and schools stores.

- Percentage of middle and high schools that offer less healthy foods as competitive foods

Because human appetite and satiation depend more on the volume of food consumed than on caloric content of the food[22], reducing the consumption of energy dense, low nutrient foods has been identified as a strategy to prevent weight gain.[23] Foods of lower energy density and higher nutrient content such as fruits and vegetables in their natural forms, nonfat/low-fat dairy products, and whole grain products are healthful alternatives to high energy density foods such as candy, cakes, salty fried snacks, and ice cream.

- Percentage of middle and high schools that allow advertising of less healthy foods

The Institute of Medicine has concluded that "food advertising to children affects their preferences, purchase behaviors, and consumption habits for different food and beverage categories, as well as for different product brands."[24] In schools, advertising can take the form of posters and signage; logos or brand names on food and beverage coolers, cups, and plates or vending machines; food sales as fundraisers, corporate sponsorship of events; advertising in school publications, and corporate sponsored classroom curricula and scholarships.24, [25] Such advertising may impact children's ability to make healthy choices in their diets.

The Community Food Environment

Lack of access to retail venues in communities to purchase healthy foods, such as supermarkets, has been associated with a lower quality diet and increased risk of obesity.[26] Likewise, some studies suggest that greater access to convenience stores and fast food restaurants, where healthy choices may not be readily available and may cost more, has been associated with greater likelihood of obesity and lower dietary quality.[26]

- Modified Retail Food Environment Index across census tracts within state
- Modified Retail Food Environment Index across impoverished census tracts within state

The modified Retail Food Environment Index (mRFEI) measures the number of healthy and less healthy food retailers in a given area. The mRFEI is based upon the Retail Food Environment Index, a measurement that has been used previously to assess the food environment and its association with obesity and diabetes, especially in areas of high poverty.[27,28]

Lower mRFEI scores for a state indicate either a greater number of census tracts that do not contain any healthy food retailers, a greater number of census tracts that contain many convenience stores and fast food restaurants relative to the number of healthy food retailers, or both.

States can work to identify areas where access to healthy food is limited. Strategies to improve the food environment in these areas can include increased access to places with healthier foods such as supermarkets and produce stores, stands and markets.[29-30] Areas without these types of healthy food retailers may still provide adequate access if smaller stores and fast food restaurants provide quality and affordable healthy foods and beverages.

Data Sources

Behavioral Indicators

Percentage of high school students who drank ≥1 sugar-sweetened soda per day

Youth Risk Behavior Survey (students in grades 9–12), 2009. Weighted percentage.

The school-based 2009 Youth Risk Behavior Survey included the following question: "During the past 7 days, how many times did you drink a can, bottle, or glass of soda or pop, such as Coke, Pepsi, or Sprite? (Do not include diet soda or diet pop.)" Response categories ranged from "I did not drink soda or pop during the past 7 days" to "4 or more times per day." National estimate is based upon a nationally representative sample of high school students and is not calculated from state estimates. Data were not available for states that did not conduct a 2009 YRBS, did not achieve a high enough overall response rate (>60%) to receive weighted results, or did not include the soda question on their 2009 YRBS questionnaire.

Available at http://www.cdc.gov/HealthyYouth/yrbs/index.htm

Percentage of high school students who watched television ≥3 hours per day

Youth Risk Behavior Survey (students in grades 9–12), 2009. Weighted percentage. The school-based 2009 Youth Risk Behavior Survey included the following question: "On an average school day, how many hours do you watch TV?" Response categories ranged from "I do not watch TV on an average school day" to "5 or more hours per day". National estimate is based upon a nationally representative sample of high school students and is not calculated from state estimates. Data were not available for states that did not conduct a 2009 YRBS, did not achieve a high enough overall response rate (>60%) to receive weighted results, or did not include the television question on their 2009 YRBS questionnaire.

Available at http://www.cdc.gov/HealthyYouth/yrbs/index.htm

Percentage of children ages 6-17 years with television in bedroom

National Survey of Children's Health, (Middle Childhood and Adolescence (6-17 years)), 2007. Weighted percentage.

The National Survey of Children's Health includes 1 question asked to parents (via telephone survey). "Is there a television in [CHILD'S

NAME] bedroom?"
Available at: http://nschdata.org/Content/Guide2007.aspx.

Percentage of children ages 12-17 who do not eat with family most days of the week

National Survey of Children's Health, (Middle Childhood and Adolescence (6-17 years)), 2007. Weighted percentage. The National Survey of Children's Health includes 1 question asked to parents (via telephone survey) "During the past week, how many days did all the family members who live in the household eat a meal together?" The percentage presented is based upon the number of parents of children ages 12-17 participating in the study who responded 0, 1, 2, or 3 days.
Available at: http://nschdata.org/Content/Guide2007.aspx.

Policy and Environmental Indicators

State regulations restrict sugar drinks in child care centers and family child care homes

States with specific regulations that apply to both child care centers and family child care homes and restrict sugar drinks. Based upon data from: "Preventing Obesity in the Child Care Setting: Evaluating State Regulations." Regulations current as of: December 2008; Date accessed: July 15, 2010.
Available at http://cfm.mc.duke.edu/child care.

State regulations require access to drinking water throughout day in child care centers and family child care homes

States with specific regulations that apply to both child care centers and family child care homes and require drinking water to be available for children throughout the day. Based upon data from: "Preventing Obesity In the Child Care Setting: Evaluating State Regulations." Regulations current as of: December 2008; Date accessed: July 15, 2010.
Available at http://cfm.mc.duke.edu/child care.

State regulations limit television and video time in child care centers and family child care homes

States with specific regulations that apply to both child care centers and family child care homes and require that television, video, and/or computer time be limited. Based upon data from: "Preventing Obesity In The Child Care

Setting: Evaluating State Regulations." Regulations current as of: December 2008; Date accessed: July 15, 2010.

Available at http://cfm.mc.duke.edu/child care.

Percentage of middle and high schools that offer sugar drinks as competitive foods

School Health Profiles, School Principal Survey, 2008. Weighted percentage. The School Health Profiles School Principal Survey includes a question regarding specific food items available as competitive foods: "Can students purchase each of the following snack foods or beverages from vending machines or at the school store, canteen, or snack bar?" The percentage presented is based upon the number of schools in each state who responded "Yes" to either response category "Soda pop or fruit drinks that are not 100% juice" or "Sports drinks, such as Gatorade." States with estimates are those with weighted data (>70% response rate). Because national estimates are not available for the Profiles survey, the data presented in the "U.S. National" row is the median of the state estimates.

Available at http://www.cdc.gov/healthyyouth/profiles/

Percentage of middle and high schools that offer less healthy foods as competitive foods

School Health Profiles, School Principal Survey, 2008. Weighted percentage.

The School Health Profiles survey includes a question regarding specific food items available as competitive foods: "Can students purchase each of the following snack foods or beverages from vending machines or at the school store, canteen, or snack bar?" The percentage presented is based upon the number of schools in each state who responded "Yes" to one or more of the following response categories: "Chocolate candy", "Other kinds of candy", "Salty snacks that are not low in fat, such as regular potato chips", "Cookies, crackers, cakes, pastries, or other baked goods that are not low in fat", "Ice cream or frozen yogurt that is not low in fat", or "Water ices or frozen slushes that do not contain juice". States with estimates are those with weighted data (>70% response rate). Because national estimates are not available for the Profiles survey, the data presented in the "U.S. National" row is the median of the state estimates. Available at http://www.cdc.gov/healthyyouth/profiles/.

Percentage of middle and high schools that allow advertising of less healthy foods

School Health Profiles, School Principal Survey, 2008. Weighted percentage.

The School Health Profiles survey includes a question regarding advertising of less healthy foods in schools: "Does this school prohibit advertisements for candy, fast food restaurants, or soft drinks in the following locations?" The percentage presented is based upon the number of schools in each state who responded "No" to one or more of the following response categories: "In the school building", "On school grounds including on the outside of the school building, on playing fields, or other areas of the campus", "On school buses or other vehicles used to transport students", or "In school publications (e.g., newsletters, newspapers, web sites, or other school publications)". States with estimates are those with weighted data (>70% response rate). Because national estimates are not available for the Profiles survey, the data presented in the "U.S. National" row is the median of the state estimates.

Available at http://www.cdc.gov/healthyyouth/profiles/.

Modified Retail Food Environment Index across census tracts within state; Modified Retail Food Environment Index across impoverished census tracts within state

The number shown is the median across census tracts within each state. Impoverished census tracts are defined as those with 20% or more individuals below the federal poverty line based upon the 2000 US Census. The data presented in the "U.S. National" row are the medians of state scores.

$$mRFEI = 100 \times \frac{\text{\# Healthy Food Retailers}}{\text{\# Healthy Food Retailers} + \text{\# Less Healthy Food Retailers}}$$

Numerator: Number of supermarkets, supercenters, and produce stores within census tracts or 1/2 mile from the tract boundary. The following stores as defined by North American Industry Classification Codes (NAICS) were included: Supermarkets and larger grocery stores (NAICS 445110; supermarkets further defined as stores with >= 50 annual payroll employees and larger grocery stores defined as stores with 10-49 employees); Fruit and Vegetable Markets (NAICS 445230); Warehouse Clubs (NAICS 452910). Fruit and vegetable markets include establishments that retail produce and includes stands, permanent stands, markets, and permanent markets. Produce is typically from wholesale but can include local. The 2007 North American Industry Classification Codes descriptions are available at http://www.census.gov/eos/www/naics/. Date accessed July 1, 2009.

Denominator: Number supermarkets, supercenters, produce stores, fast food restaurants, and convenience stores within census tracts or 1/2 mile from the tract boundary. Supermarkets, supercenters, and produce stores were defined as in the numerator.

Fast food stores were defined according to NAICS code 722211(fast food restaurants). Convenience stores were defined according to NAICS code 445120 (convenience stores) or NAICS code 445110 (small groceries) where the number of employees was 3 or fewer.

Data sources: Supermarkets, supercenters, and produce store data is derived from InfoUSA business database, 2009. Fast food retail data is from NavTeq database, 2009. Convenience store data is from Homeland Security Information Program database, 2008.

State	Behavioral Indicators			
	% HS Students Who Drank ≥1 Soda/Day	% HS Students Who Watched 3+ Hours of TV/Day	% Children Ages 6-17 with TV in Bedroom	% Children Ages 12-17 Not Eating Family Meals Most Days of Week
U.S. National	29.2	32.8	50.2	30.7
Alabama	38.8	37.8	67.7	39.0
Alaska	20.1	24.8	33.0	28.7
Arizona	28.1	33.3	47.3	27.9
Arkansas	33.5	36.4	65.9	30.7
California			46.4	26.7
Colorado	24.6	25.1	36.6	23.9
Connecticut		30.2	42.9	32.6
Delaware	28.8	37.7	51.9	34.9
D.C.			58.8	35.7
Florida	28.6	38.2	61.4	27.3
Georgia	29.7	39.2	56.1	31.0
Hawaii	20.8	30.1	39.3	25.0
Idaho	18.3	21.9	35.2	27.6
Illinois	31.1	35.7	50.9	34.9
Indiana	29.7	29.0	52.8	33.5
Iowa			43.9	31.7
Kansas	30.7	28.3	43.1	32.7
Kentucky	35.7	28.8	62.4	32.1
Louisiana	36.6	40.3	70.6	37.7
Maine		25.4	39.9	30.7
Maryland	21.3	39.1	46.0	31.8
Massachusetts	21.0	30.4	36.3	30.0
Michigan	27.6	29.6	47.5	28.0
Minnesota			30.5	34.4
Mississippi	40.2	44.9	69.3	32.8
Missouri	31.5	32.4	52.5	33.2

| State | Behavioral Indicators | | | |
	% HS Students Who Drank ≥1 Soda/Day	% HS Students Who Watched 3+ Hours of TV/Day	% Children Ages 6-17 with TV in Bedroom	% Children Ages 12-17 Not Eating Family Meals Most Days of Week
Montana	25.7	23.7	36.3	26.3
Nebraska			40.5	31.7
Nevada	22.1	35.1	59.1	28.0
New Hampshire	22.1	23.0	35.5	29.5
New Jersey	19.9	32.6	48.5	30.5
New Mexico	30.4	32.6	50.0	23.5
New York	24.5	32.7	48.9	33.2
North Carolina	32.5	36.2	58.2	28.3
North Dakota	26.3	25.6	43.1	27.7
Ohio			51.0	30.4
Oklahoma	38.1	29.0	58.8	27.3
Oregon			41.6	27.5
Pennsylvania	25.7	30.8	50.9	33.7
Rhode Island	21.2	29.1	47.7	32.0
South Carolina	33.2	39.7	60.6	34.9
South Dakota	28.8	22.6	38.2	29.1
Tennessee	41.3	37.7	61.2	35.1
Texas	32.8	36.3	54.2	33.7
Utah	14.5	16.3	24.4	22.3
Vermont	22.9		31.0	25.9
Virginia			47.6	33.3
Washington			32.0	25.8
West Virginia	34.5	31.5	66.7	27.0
Wisconsin	23.1	23.1	40.4	33.3
Wyoming	27.0	22.0	41.5	26.6

Data were not available for states that did not conduct a 2009 YRBS, did not achieve a high enough overall response rate (≥60%) to receive weighted results, or did not include the television or soda question on their 2009 YRBS questionnaire.

State	Child Care Environment			School Environment			Community Environment	
	Regulations to Restrict Sugar Drinks	Regulations to Require Access to Drinking Water Throughout Day	Regulations to Limit Screen Time	% Middle & High Schools That Offer Sugar Drinks as Competitive Foods	% Middle & High Schools That Offer Less Healthy Competitive Foods	% Middle & High Schools That Allow Advertising of Less Healthy Foods	Modified Retail Food Environment Index	Modified Retail Food Environment Index – Impoverished Census Tracts
U.S. National	2 states	27 states	18 states	64.4*	51.4*	49.0*	10	7
Alabama	No	No	Yes	67.2	35.6	49.0	10	8
Alaska	No	No	Yes	53.2	41.8	40.8	6	0
Arizona	No	No	No	47.5	33.9	35.1	12	10
Arkansas	No	Yes	No	57.4	35.7	55.5	9	9
California	No	No	No	59.5	32.5	31.9	11	10
Colorado	No	Yes	Yes	69.8	63.3	52.2	11	8
Connecticut	No	Yes	No	16.7	30.7	28.9	6	4
Delaware	No	Yes	Yes	58.0	44.1	38.0	12	5
D.C.	No	No	No				4	4
Florida	No	No	No	72.4	58.6	51.5	10	8
Georgia	Yes	Yes	Yes				8	7
Hawaii	No	Yes	No	24.1	22.3	39.2	14	14
Idaho	No	No	No	66.4	67.0	59.9	13	13
Illinois	No	Yes	No	55.2	47.7	50.9	8	6
Indiana	No	Yes	No	71.9	65.0	64.0	10	6
Iowa	No	No	No	77.6	53.9	56.1	10	6
Kansas	No	No	Yes	80.3	62.7	65.8	10	7
Kentucky	No	No	Yes	48.6	33.4	68.2	10	8
Louisiana	No	No	No				9	7
Maine	No	No	Yes	56.0	34.1	30.8	15	15
Maryland	No	No	Yes	56.2	57.0	41.5	10	4
Massachusetts	No	Yes	No	46.3	46.5	28.6	7	5
Michigan	No	No	Yes	69.9	64.9	41.4	10	8

State	Child Care Environment			School Environment			Community Environment	
	Regulations to Restrict Sugar Drinks	Regulations to Require Access to Drinking Water Throughout Day	Regulations to Limit Screen Time	% Middle & High Schools That Offer Sugar Drinks as Competitive Foods	% Middle & High Schools That Offer Less Healthy Competitive Foods	% Middle & High Schools That Allow Advertising of Less Healthy Foods	Modified Retail Food Environment Index	Modified Retail Food Environment Index – Impoverished Census Tracts
Minnesota	No	Yes	No	65.9	58.3	49.0	10	8
Mississippi	No	No	Yes	56.2	40.5	48.0	8	8
Missouri	No	Yes	No	79.3	56.3	61.1	10	8
Montana	No	Yes	No	76.3	50.9	66.8	16	14
Nebraska	No	No	No	74.0	53.7	66.7	10	9
Nevada	Yes	Yes	No	70.8	40.8	37.8	11	10
New Hampshire	No	No	No	59.5	51.7	40.1	9	7
New Jersey	No	Yes	No	44.4	43.9	26.6	8	5
New Mexico	No	No	Yes				12	10
New York	No	Yes	No	66.8	58.5	23.6	8	6
North Carolina	No	Yes	No	65.0	54.7	58.5	11	9
North Dakota	No	No	No	63.3	37.9	54.7	8	0
Ohio	No	Yes	No	72.0	67.0	69.2	9	6
Oklahoma	No	Yes	Yes	76.1	59.8	65.4	6	6
Oregon	No	No	No	55.0	54.3	52.0	13	14
Pennsylvania	No	Yes	No	54.7	46.9	47.6	11	5
Rhode Island	No	Yes	No	48.8	41.4	27.6	5	5
South Carolina	No	Yes	Yes	71.9	61.9	54.2	9	6
South Dakota	No	No	No	76.3	41.5	59.0	8	0
Tennessee	No	Yes	Yes	36.3	36.2	56.3	10	7
Texas	No	Yes	No	56.0	54.9	46.6	7	7
Utah	No	Yes	No	81.0	83.4	46.5	13	11
Vermont	No	Yes	Yes	53.2	50.9	41.8	13	0
Virginia	No	Yes	No	64.4	61.2	47.6	11	7

(Continued)

State	Child Care Environment			School Environment			Community Environment	
	Regulations to Restrict Sugar Drinks	Regulations to Require Access to Drinking Water Throughout Day	Regulations to Limit Screen Time	% Middle & High Schools That Offer Sugar Drinks as Competitive Foods	% Middle & High Schools That Offer Less Healthy Competitive Foods	% Middle & High Schools That Allow Advertising of Less Healthy Foods	Modified Retail Food Environment Index	Modified Retail Food Environment Index – Impoverished Census Tracts
Washington	No	No	No	68.0	56.0	44.1	12	11
West Virginia	No	Yes	Yes	43.6	40.8	51.1	13	11
Wisconsin	No	No	Yes	72.1	58.7	56.6	11	6
Wyoming	No	No	No	71.3	51.4	66.5	10	8

*Because national estimates are not available for these variables, the data presented in the "U.S. National" row is the median of the state estimates

Data were not available for states that did not achieve a high enough overall response rate (≥70%) on the 2008 School Health Profiles Survey to receive weighted results.

End Notes

[1] U.S. Department of Agriculture and U.S. Department of Health and Human Services. Dietary Guidelines for Americans, 2010. 7th Edition, Washington, DC: U.S. Government Printing Office, December 2010. http://www.cnpp.usda.gov/DGAs2010-PolicyDocument.htm. Accessed January 31, 2011.

[2] Reedy J, Krebs-Smith SM. Dietary sources of energy, solid fats, and added sugars among children and adolescents in the United States. J Am Diet Assoc 2010;110(10):1477-84.

[3] Healthy People, Office of Disease Prevention and Health Promotion, U.S. Department of Health and Human Services, DC, www.healthypeople.gov. Accessed January 31,2011.

[4] American Academy of Pediatrics. Committee on Public Education. American Academy of Pediatrics: Children, adolescents, and television. Pediatrics 2001;107(2):423-6.

[5] Rao G. Childhood obesity: highlights of AMA Expert Committee recommendations. Am Fam Physician 2008;78(1):56-63.

[6] Vartanian LR, Schwartz MB, Brownell KD. Effects of Soft Drink Consumption on Nutrition and Health: A Systematic Review and Meta-Analysis. Am J Public Health 2007;97(4):667-675.

[7] Centers for Disease Control and Prevention (CDC). Television and video viewing time among children aged 2 years - Oregon, 2006-2007. MMWR Morb Mortal Wkly Rep 2010;59 (27):837-41.

[8] Adachi-Mejia AM, Longacre MR, Gibson JJ, et al. Children with a TV in their bedroom at higher risk for being overweight. Int J Obes (Lond) 2007;31(4):644-51.

[9] Zimmerman FJ, Bell JF. Associations of television content type and obesity in children. Am J Public Health. 2010;100(2):334- 40.

[10] Robinson TN. Television viewing and childhood obesity. Pediatr Clin North Am 2001;Aug;48(4):1017-25.

[11] Klesges RC, Stein RJ, Eck LH, Isbell TR, Klesges LM. Parental influence on food selection in young children and its relationships to childhood obesity. Am J Clin Nutr 1991;53(4):859-64.

[12] Larson NI, Neumark-Sztainer D, Hannan PJ, Story M. Family meals during adolescence are associated with higher diet quality and healthful meal patterns during young adulthood. J Am Diet Assoc 2007;107(9):1502-10.

[13] Gable S, Chang Y, Krull JL. Television watching and frequency of family meals are predictive of overweight onset and persistence in a national sample of school-aged children. J Am Diet Assoc 2007;107(1):53-61.

[14] Guthrie JF, Lin BH, Frazao E. Role of food prepared away from home in the American diet, 1977-78 versus 1994-96: changes and consequences. J Nutr Educ Behav 2002;34(3):140-50.

[15] Keener D, Goodman K et al (2009). Recommended community strategies and measurements to prevent obesity in the United States: Implementation and measurement guide. Atlanta, GA: U.S. DHHS, Centers for Disease Control and Prevention. http://www.cdc.gov/obesity/downloads/community strategies guide.pdf

[16] IOM (Institute of Medicine). 2009. Local Government Actions to Prevent Childhood Obesity. Washington, DC: The National Academies Press. http://www.iom.edu/Object.File/Master/72/800/local%20govts%20obesity%20report%20brief%20FINAL%20for%20web.pdf

[17] IOM (Institute of Medicine). 2007. Nutrition Standards for Foods in Schools: Leading the Way Toward Healthier Youth. Washington, DC: The National Academies Press. http://www.iom.edu/CMS/3788/30181/42502.aspx

[18] America's Children: Key National Indicators of Well-Being, 2009. Federal Interagency Forum on Child and Family Statistics. http://www.childstats.gov/americaschildren/famsoc3.asp

[19] Wang YC, Ludwig DS, Sonneville K, Gortmaker SL. Impact of change in sweetened caloric beverage consumption on energy intake among children and adolescents. Arch Pediatr Adolesc Med 2009; 163(4):336-43.

[20] Harris JL, Pomeranz JL, Lobstein T, et al. A crisis in the marketplace: how food marketing contributes to childhood obesity and what can be done. Annu Rev Public Health 2009;30:211-25.

[21] Ranjit N, Evans MH, Byrd-Williams C, Evans AE, Hoelscher DM. Dietary and activity correlates of sugar-sweetened beverage consumption among adolescents. Pediatrics 2010;126(4):e754-61.

[22] Bell EA, Castellanos VH, Pelkman CL, et al. Energy density of foods affects energy intake in normal-weight women. Am J Clin Nutr 1998;67(3):412-20.

[23] Rolls BJ. The relationship between dietary energy density and energy intake. Physiol Behav. 2009;97(5):609-15.

[24] IOM (Institute of Medicine). 2005. Food Marketing to Children and Youth: Threat or Opportunity? Washington, DC: The National Academies Press.

[25] Public Health Institute. 2006. The Food and Beverage Marketing on California High School Campuses Survey. http://www.phi.org/news LEAN/marketing report.pdf

[26] Larson NI, Story MT, Nelson MC. Neighborhood environments: disparities in access to healthy foods in the U.S. Am J Prev Med 2009;36(1):74-81.

[27] California Center for Public Health Advocacy (CCPHA). Designed for Disease: The Link Between Local Food Environments and Obesity and Diabetes. 2008. http://www.publichealthadvocacy.org/designedfordisease.html. Accessed July 12, 2010.

[28] California Center for Public Health Advocacy (CCPHA). Searching for Healthy Food: The Food Landscape in California Cities and Counties. 2007. http://www.publichealth advocacy.org/searchingforhealthyfood.html. Accessed July 12, 2010.

[29] Seymour JD, Fenley MA, Yaroch AL, et al. Fruit and vegetable environment, policy, and pricing workshop: introduction to the conference proceedings. Prev Med 2004;39(2)S71–4.

[30] Story M, Kaphingst KM, Robinson-O'Brien R, et al. Creating healthy food and eating environments: policy and environmental approaches. Annu Rev Public Health 2008;29:253–72.

In: Weighty Factors in Children's Food...   ISBN: 978-1-62257-917-4
Editors: C.E. Oyler and C. De Volld   © 2013 Nova Science Publishers, Inc.

Chapter 4

TAXING CALORIC SWEETENED BEVERAGES: POTENTIAL EFFECTS ON BEVERAGE CONSUMPTION, CALORIE INTAKE, AND OBESITY*

Travis A. Smith, Biing-Hwan Lin and Jonq-Ying Lee

ABSTRACT

The link between high U.S. obesity rates and the overconsumption of added sugars, largely from sodas and fruit drinks, has prompted public calls for a tax on caloric sweetened beverages. Faced with such a tax, consumers may reduce consumption of these sweetened beverages and substitute nontaxed beverages, such as bottled water, juice, and milk. This study estimated that a tax-induced 20-percent price increase on caloric sweetened beverages could cause an average reduction of 37 calories per day, or 3.8 pounds of body weight over a year, for adults and an average of 43 calories per day, or 4.5 pounds over a year, for children. Given these reductions in calorie consumption, results show an estimated decline in adult overweight prevalence (66.9 to 62.4 percent) and obesity prevalence (33.4 to 30.4 percent), as well as the child at-risk-for-overweight prevalence (32.3 to 27.0 percent) and the overweight prevalence (16.6 to 13.7 percent). Actual impacts would depend on many

---

* This is an edited, reformatted and augmented version of the United States Department of Agriculture, Economic Research Report No. 100, dated July 2010.

factors, including how the tax is reflected in consumer prices and the competitive strategies of beverage manufacturers and food retailers.

Keywords: Sugar-sweetened beverages (SSB), soft drinks, soda tax, added sugars, obesity, and beverage demand

SUMMARY

The prevalence of obesity among the U.S. population has increased markedly over the past three decades. Latest figures indicate that two-thirds of adults are either overweight or obese, and growing numbers of children are overweight as well. Associations between obesity and certain dietary trends, such as eating away from home and drinking beverages sweetened with sugar and/ or high-fructose and other corn syrups (e.g., sodas, fruit drinks, sports and energy drinks, and powdered mixes) have received increasing attention.

What Is the Issue?

According to 1999-2004 National Health and Nutrition Examination Survey (NHANES) data on food intake, the average American consumed 22.5 teaspoons of added sugar per day, with almost half attributed to sodas and fruit drinks. Under a 2,400-calorie diet conforming to the 2005 *Dietary Guidelines for Americans*, 22.5 teaspoons of added sugars nearly exhausts the discretionary calorie allowance. High U.S. obesity rates have prompted the Institute of Medicine of the National Academies of Sciences and some State and local government officials to suggest a tax on caloric sweetened beverages. This study examines the potential effects of such a tax on total beverage consumption, calorie intake, and the prevalence of overweight and obesity among Americans.

What Did the Study Find?

This study analyzed the effects of a hypothetical tax on caloric sweetened sodas, fruit drinks, sports and energy drinks, and powdered mixes. The study found that consumers facing a higher price induced by a tax would react by adjusting their choices among alternative beverages, such as diet drinks, bottled water, juice, coffee/tea, or milk. Results suggest that:

- A tax-induced 20-percent increase in the price of caloric sweetened beverages could reduce net calorie intake from all beverages by 37 calories per day for the average adult. The effects for children were estimated to be larger—an average reduction of 43 calories per day.
- By assuming that 1 pound of body fat has about 3,500 calories, and assuming all else remains equal, the daily calorie reductions would translate into an average reduction of 3.8 pounds over a year for adults and 4.5 pounds over a year for children.
- The weight loss induced by the tax could reduce the overweight prevalence among adults from 66.9 to 62.4 percent and the prevalence of obesity from 33.4 to 30.4 percent. For children, the at-risk-of-overweight prevalence would decline from 32.3 to 27.0 percent and the overweight prevalence would decline from 16.6 to 13.7 percent.

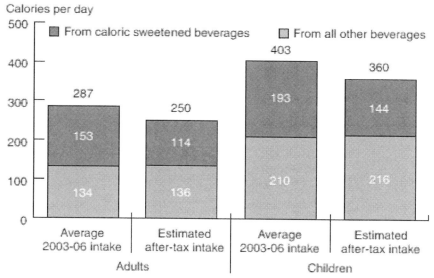

Source: Economic Research Service calculations based on the National Health and Examination Survey data, 2003-06.

A 20-percent price increase from a tax on caloric sweetened beverages is estimated to reduce total calorie intake from beverages by 13 percent for adults and by 11 percent for children.

These reductions in the proportion of overweight and obese Americans are the result of two factors:

1. A large group of individuals are overweight or obese by only a few pounds, and a small reduction in calorie intake could change their weight classification; and
2. Many overweight and obese Americans consume large amounts of caloric sweetened beverages. For example, 10.6 percent of overweight adults consumed more than 450 calories per day from caloric sweetened beverages—nearly three times the average amount of 152 calories consumed by adults.

A tax on caloric sweetened beverages would affect all those who consume them—overweight, obese, and healthy weight individuals. Our estimates of changes in overweight and obesity rates do not capture potential improvements in weight status among those with healthier weights. There are many individuals, however, who are a few pounds shy of the Body Mass Index (BMI) cutoffs for overweight and obese. The tax-induced reduction in calorie intake could not only reduce obesity rates but also help keep certain borderline individuals from joining the ranks of the obese or overweight.

The estimated impact of these measures would depend on, among other factors, the size and type of tax and how the tax is reflected in the prices consumers pay. Manufacturers' and retailers' responses to the tax would affect how much of the tax is passed on to consumers. Differences in the at-home and away-from-home food markets are also likely to influence how a tax would affect prices consumers pay (e.g., bottled and canned soda purchases in grocery stores versus free beverage refills from soda fountains in fast food restaurants).

How Was the Study Conducted?

Two national datasets were used in this analysis: (1) actual consumer grocery purchases of beverages from 1998-2007 Nielsen Homescan panels, and (2) individual daily beverage intake data with corresponding measured height and weight from the 2003-06 National Health and Nutrition Examination Survey (NHANES). Beverages in each dataset were grouped into eight categories based on calorie content (caloric sweetened beverages, diet drinks, skim milk, low-fat milk, whole milk, 100 percent fruit and vegetable juice, coffee/tea, and bottled water). Using the purchase data, a demand system was specified to estimate how beverage-purchasing decisions would change as a result of a price increase for caloric sweetened beverages. Price elasticity estimates were then applied to individual beverage intake data reported in NHANES to estimate changes in caloric intake for each beverage category in response to a tax-induced 20-percent increase in the price of caloric sweetened beverages. By calculating changes in calorie consumption among all beverages and assuming that 1 pound of body fat has about 3,500 calories, we estimated the change in each NHANES respondent's body weight to calculate after-tax overweight and obesity prevalence in the U.S. population.

BACKGROUND

Obesity prevalence among the U.S. population has increased markedly over the past three decades, with the latest figures indicating that two-thirds of U.S. adults are either overweight or obese, and growing numbers of children are either overweight or at risk for overweight (fig. 1). Some research suggests that if current obesity rates persist, 86 percent of American adults will be either overweight or obese by 2030 (Wang et al., 2008). According to a quantitative review of the literature, Tsai et al. (2010) concluded that the U.S. national aggregate medical costs (in 2008 dollars) of overweight was $15.8 billion and obesity was $98.1 billion, totaling $113.9 billion. As researchers evaluate American weight gain and intervention strategies to tackle this health problem, associations between obesity and certain dietary trends, such as eating out and drinking caloric sweetened beverages, have received greater attention.

According to two systematic reviews of the literature, consumption of beverages sweetened with sugar and/or high-fructose and other corn syrups is linked to risks for obesity and type 2 diabetes (Malik et al., 2006; Vartanian et al., 2007).

Positive associations between weight gain and caloric sweetened beverage consumption, however, do not necessarily imply causality (Dietz, 2006). Nevertheless, caloric sweetened beverages have been targeted as part of a tax policy to reduce calorie intake, improve diet and health, and generate revenue that governments can use to address obesity-related health and economic burdens (Brownell and Frieden, 2009; Jacobson and Brownell, 2000; Powell and Chaloupka, 2009; Institute of Medicine, 2009).

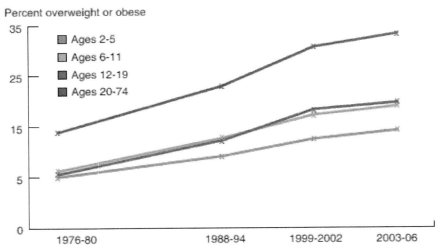

Source: Centers for Disease Control and Prevention (CDC), National Health and Nutrition Examination Surveys (NHANES).

Notes: Overweight children (ages 2-19) are defined by sex- and age-specific BMI ≥ 95th percentile based on Centers for Disease Control and Prevention growth charts (CDC, 2009b); obese adults (ages 20-74) are defined by a BMI of ≥ 30.

Figure 1. Overweight and obesity rates, 1976-2006.

In 2009, 33 States levied sales taxes on sodas, both nondiet and diet, at an average rate of 5.2 percent (Bridging the Gap, 2010). Missouri, Virginia, and Utah had the lowest soda sales tax rates at less than 2 percent, while the highest rates (7 percent) were assessed in Indiana, Mississippi, New Jersey, and Rhode Island. Thirteen other States had tax rates of at least 6 percent. Many States also implemented similar taxes on vending machine sales, or levied additional taxes on manufacturers, distributors, wholesalers, or retailers of sodas (see Appendix Tables 1 and 2 for more information). Recent studies investigating links between State-level soda taxes and Body Mass Index (BMI)[1] among children and adolescents (Powell et al., 2009; Sturm et al., 2010; Fletcher et al., 2010), as well as adults (Fletcher et al., 2008), have shown little-to-no association.

These findings of minimal effects of State-level soda sales taxes on weight outcomes are not surprising. Soda sales taxes are generally small and infrequently changed, whereas BMI has been growing until recent years. Moreover, a sales tax is not reflected in the shelf price; it is rung up at the checkout counter with other food purchases. As a result, consumers may be unaware of the tax and unresponsive to a sales tax increase when making retail purchases (McLaughlin, 2009).

Proponents of taxing caloric sweetened beverages suggest that relatively higher tax rates are necessary to have measurable effects, as in the case of tobacco taxation (Engelhard et al, 2009). For example, Brownell and colleagues (2009) propose "an excise tax of 1 cent per ounce for beverages that have any added caloric sweetener." Assuming the tax would be wholly passed on to the consumer, their proposed tax rate could range widely depending on brand, container size, and sale price. For example, a 12-pack of 12-ounce cans of branded soda priced at $6 would carry a tax of $1.44 (24 percent), while a discounted 2-liter container of soda priced at $1 would carry a tax of $0.68 (68 percent).

Taxing food to reduce consumption hinges on the fundamental economic principle that consumers respond to a higher price by purchasing less. Therefore, the success of a beverage tax partly depends on how much consumers curtail their consumption in response to the higher beverage price (own-price elasticity). A recent review of food demand research revealed an own-price elasticity for sodas and other beverages of -0.8 to -1.0, depending on category definitions (Andreyeva et al., 2009).[2] This elasticity range has been used to predict consumers' responses to taxing sodas in recent studies (Brownell et al., 2009; Chaloupka et al., 2009). Yale University's Rudd Center for Food Policy and Obesity uses an own-price elasticity of -1.2 to calculate the revenues generated by a tax on caloric sweetened beverages (Rudd Center, 2010).

For our evaluation, deficiencies in these reported elasticities exist. First, consumers will respond to a particular beverage tax by adjusting their purchases of alternative beverages (cross-price elasticity). Without estimates of cross-price elasticities, researchers have relied solely on the own-price elasticity and assumed away cross-price effects (Brownell et al., 2009; Chaloupka et al., 2009). Secondly, many studies have included sodas and/ or fruit drinks in their analysis, but have not differentiated between nondiet and diet (e.g., Kinnucan et al., 2001; Yen et al., 2004; Zheng and Kaiser, 2008). To estimate reductions in energy intake and obesity, a distinction must be made between caloric sweetened beverages and their low-calorie counterparts. Few demand studies to date have separated regular soft drinks from their low-calorie counterparts—one did not include cross-price effects of alternative beverages (Bergtold et al., 2004), while another examined only soft drinks (Dhar et al., 2003) and excluded sweetened sports, energy, and fruit drinks. As a result, the literature lacks the demand elasticity estimates needed to fully examine the effect of taxing caloric sweetened beverages.

In this study, the previous limitations are addressed by analyzing grocery purchases from a panel of American households over a 10-year period (1998-2007). Specifically, we estimate a beverage demand system in which all beverage purchases are categorized by calorie content. The estimated demand elasticities are then applied to individuals' beverage intake data from a nationally representative survey, which enables us to estimate changes in calorie consumption due to changes in purchasing decisions when the price of caloric sweetened beverages increases as a result of a tax. The national intake survey data are ideal for this study because, in addition to intake data, they have a nutrient database for all beverages consumed, as well as measured height and weight for each respondent. By calculating the net change in calorie consumption after consumers adjust their after-tax beverage purchases, we can estimate the reduction in body weight, and thus, overweight and obesity prevalence in the U.S. population.

TRENDS IN U.S. BEVERAGE CONSUMPTION, 1977–2006

Total calorie intake among the U.S. population has increased over the past 30 years (USDA/ERS-Nutrient Availability, 2010). The majority of the increase comes from snacking on both food and beverages (Piernas and Popkin, 2009). A previous study found that the percentage of total calorie intake from beverages increased from 14.2 to 21.0 percent over 1997-2002, largely from caloric sweetened beverages (Duffey and Popkin, 2007). Because caloric intake from beverages is less satiating compared with solid foods (DiMeglio and Mattes, 2000; Mattes, 1996, 2006; Stull et al., 2008) and many caloric sweetened beverages lack sufficient nutrient content, the link between sweetened beverage consumption and weight gain has attracted attention (Dennis et al., 2009).

Trends in American beverage consumption have changed dramatically over the past three decades (fig. 2). The popularity of caloric sweetened sodas and fruit drinks in American diets has increased at the expense of milk, especially since the late 1980s. Today, adults consume nearly twice as many ounces of caloric sweetened sodas as milk. Children's milk consumption was over three times that of their soda consumption in the late 1970s, but children consumed roughly equal amounts of each beverage by 2003-06. Further, the consumption of fruit drinks has been on the rise for both adults and children.

These consumption trends correlate with the prevalence of overweight children and obese adults in the United States and have prompted a call for caloric sweetened beverages to be consumed more judiciously in lieu of more nutritious beverages (e.g., milk and juices) or low-calorie beverages (e.g., water and diet drinks).

Daily milk consumption among children has declined to similar consumption levels as nondiet sodas, while nondiet soda consumption among adults surpasses milk

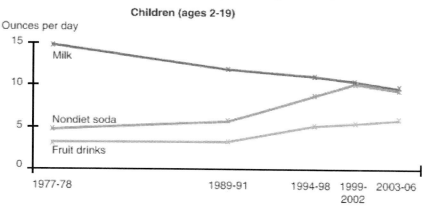

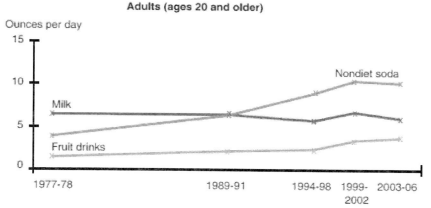

Source: ERS calculations based on USDA's 1977-78 Nationwide Food Consumption Survey (NFCS) data, 1989-91 and 1994-98 Continuing Survey of Food Intakes by Individuals (CSFII), and the Centers for Disease Control and Prevention's (CDC) National Center for Health Statistics 1999-2006 National Health and Nutrition Examination Survey (NHANES).

Figure 2. Beverage consumption, 1977-2006.

CONSUMPTION OF ADDED SUGARS
BY THE AMERICAN POPULATION

Every 5 years, the U.S. Government updates the *Dietary Guidelines for Americans* to help consumers choose diets that meet their nutritional needs. The *Guidelines* set recommended consumption amounts for the major food groups. The *Guidelines* do not include recommendations for added sugars, but instead include a "discretionary calorie allowance" for diets that include and do not exceed the recommended amounts of each food group in the *Guidelines* (*Dietary Guidelines for Americans,* Appendix A-3, 2005). Added sugars include cane and beet sugars, honey, molasses, and corn and other syrups used for home baking and sweetening, as well as sugars commonly added to processed foods and beverages, but not the naturally occurring sugars in fruit or milk.

For diets following the *Guidelines*, the discretionary calorie allowance may be used to increase the amount of food selected from each food group; to consume foods that are not in the lowest fat form (such as 2 percent milk or medium-fat meat); to add oil, fat, or sugars to foods; to consume alcohol; or to consume foods that contain added sugars (*Dietary Guidelines for Americans,* 2005). Like the recommendations for major food groups, the allowance is based on an individual's energy (calorie) requirement which, in turn, is determined by age, gender, body weight and height, physical activity level, and pregnancy/lactation status. For example, a 2,400-calorie diet conforming to the *Guidelines,* which may be appropriate for a moderately active adult male with a median height and weight for that height (BMI=22.5), includes a discretionary allowance of 362 calories, which is equivalent to roughly 23 teaspoons (tsp) of added sugars. Likewise, a moderately active 4 to 8 year old child on a 1,400-calorie diet conforming to the *Guidelines* would have 171 discretionary calories, equal to about 11 tsp of added sugars. The *Guidelines* leave it to the individual to decide how to consume these calories, including whether to allocate them to the consumption of food and beverages with added sugars.

Using data from 1999-2004 NHANES, we found that the average American consumed 22.5 tsp of added sugars per day (table 1)—essentially exhausting the 362 discretionary calorie allowance for a 2,400-calorie diet following the *Guidelines,* leaving no allowance for other foods. American adults consumed 21.6 tsp of added sugars per day and children (ages 2–19) consumed 24.9 tsp. Caloric sweetened sodas and fruit drinks (containing less than 100 percent juice by volume) are major sources of added sugars in American diets, contributing an average of 10.58 tsp of added sugars each day. Children consumed 11.96 tsp of added sugars from sodas and fruit drinks per day (47 percent of their total intake of added sugars).

The excessive intake of added sugars from sodas and fruit drinks, and its correlation with weight gain, has been receiving attention in the fight against obesity. Recognizing the role of caloric sweetened beverages in American children's diets, the Institute of Medicine (2009) recommended that local governments implement a tax strategy for calorie-dense, nutrient-poor foods and beverages to discourage consumption. Earlier this year, the White House Task Force on Childhood Obesity recommended that Federal and State/local governments analyze the effects of taxes on less healthy, energy-dense foods, such as caloric sweetened beverages (White House Task Force on Childhood Obesity, 2010). The Institute of Medicine and other beverage tax advocates (IOM, 2009; Brownell et al., 2009; Brownell and Frieden, 2009) suggest that the generated tax revenues could be used to promote healthier eating and reduce or prevent obesity.

Table 1. Added sugar consumption, 1999-2004

Caloric sweetened soft drinks and fruit drinks account for almost half of added sugars in the American diet

Population	Sodas	Fruit drinks	Other drinks	Desserts	Ready to-eat cereals	Sweets	Other foods	Total added sugars
Teaspoons per day								
United States								
(age 2 and older)	8.2	2.4	0.8	3.7	0.8	3.3	3.2	22.5
Children (ages 2-19)	8.4	3.6	0.6	3.6	1.5	3.9	3.4	24.9
Adults (age 20 and older)	8.1	2.0	0.9	3.7	0.6	3.1	3.1	21.6

Source: ERS calculations based on National Health and Nutrition Examination Survey (NHANES) 1999-2004 data.

Notes: Desserts include dairy foods (e.g., ice cream, custards, and puddings) and sweetened grains (e.g., cakes, cookies, pies, and pastries). Sweets include candies, jams, jellies, sugar, honey, and other sweeteners. Totals may not sum due to rounding.

POTENTIAL TAX-INDUCED CHANGES IN CALORIE INTAKE FROM BEVERAGES

Using grocery purchase data reported by Nielsen Homescan panelists between 1998 and 2007 (Nielsen, 2007), we estimated a beverage demand system. Household grocery purchases were aggregated into 120 national monthly obser-vations. Beverage purchases were grouped into eight categories using product descriptions provided by Nielsen as shown in table 2. We also present the average daily calorie intake for adults and children in each beverage category.

For caloric sweetened beverages, we found the own-price elasticity of demand to be -1.26 (see, "Appendix: Beverage Demand Model" for full econometric details and demand elasticity estimates). Thus, a 10-percent increase in price is predicted to reduce grocery store purchases of caloric sweetened beverages by 12.6 percent (see box, "Effect of Beverage Tax May Differ in the Away-From-Home Market"). Faced with a higher price for caloric sweetened beverages, consumers would purchase more bottled water, juice, and milk. Bottled water was found to be the strongest substitute for caloric sweetened beverages (cross-price elasticity of 0.75), while skim and whole milk were the weakest substitutes (cross-price elasticity of 0.2). Fruit and vegetable juices containing 100 percent juice were also found to be substitutes for caloric sweetened beverages with a cross-price elasticity of 0.56, falling between that of water and milk. A complementary effect for diet beverages was found (cross-price elasticity of -0.46), suggesting a higher price for caloric sweetened beverages would decrease grocery purchases of diet drinks. Given that our estimates are based on household-level grocery purchases, the complimentary effect is possibly the result of a diverse set of preferences within a household for diet and nondiet sweetened beverages.

We use the demand elasticities to estimate changes in individuals' daily beverage consumption reported in 2003-06 NHANES in response to a tax-induced price increase of caloric sweetened beverages. Individual daily beverage consumption and the corresponding caloric contents are aggregated into eight categories, as specified in table 2, using USDA's nutrient database (USDA/ARS, 2010). Certain juices and milk drinks are more energy dense than sodas (fig. 3). Because we expect consumers to adjust their consumption of alternative beverages when a tax is levied on caloric sweetened beverages (cross-price elasticity), failure to incorporate alternative bever ages would bias an assessment of the calorie-reduction effect from a tax. Furthermore, not including alternative beverages to estimate a beverage demand system would result in model misspecification and bias estimates of demand elasticities.

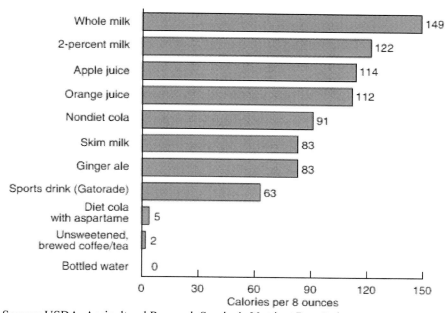

Source: USDA, Agricultural Research Service's Nutrient Data Laboratory.

Figure 3. Calorie content varies widely across beverages.

Effect of Beverage Tax May Differ in the Away-From-Home Market

Our results are based on a few assumptions typically found in demand studies. Like many other beverage demand studies, we used data from household purchases at grocery stores and did not include beverage purchases from other commercial outlets, such as restaurants and vending machines. One cannot ignore, however, the large amount of beverages purchased in eating establishments, such as fast food and full-service restaurants, ball games, movie theaters, and other away-from-home eating occasions.

According to 2003-06 NHANES, about 50 percent of caloric sweetened beverages were consumed away from home.

> In fast food and full-service restaurants, consumers often pay for a meal combo that includes beverages. Likewise, some restaurants offer free refills, creating a disconnect between quantity purchased and price. Because of these marketing conditions, consumers are likely to react differently to a price increase at home than away from home. While we acknowledge this potential problem, we note the difficulty in estimating the away-fromhome demand for beverages due to data deficiencies. In this study, at-home elasticities are applied to total at-home and away-from-home consumption. This assumption has been made, but not pointed out, in past studies that estimate the impact of a tax on beverage consumption.

Assuming that a tax raises caloric sweetened beverage prices at retail food stores and restaurants by 20 percent for consumers, the average daily calorie intake from caloric sweetened beverages is estimated to fall by 38.8 calories for adults and by 48.8 calories for children (table 3). To calculate the net change in calorie consumption from shifting beverage choices in response to a tax, we apply the cross-price effects to individual beverage intake data found in NHANES. Led by increased consumption of calorie-containing juices and milk after the tax is imposed, average daily calorie intake from all beverages other than caloric sweetened beverages increased an estimated 1.9 calories for adults and 6.1 calories for children. Subtracting these calorie increases from the calorie savings from lower consumption of the taxed beverages results in a net decline of 36.9 calories per day for adults and 42.7 calories per day for children[3] (see box, "Calculating Changes in Calorie Consumption and Weight Status").

Our findings are based on a historical snapshot of household beverage purchases linked with individual beverage intake surveys. From these historical purchase transactions, we have estimated the price elasticity of demand—how consumers would react to a price change in caloric sweetened beverages. Price elasticities are generally used to simulate the effects of a "small" change in price because, like our estimates, they are typically derived with data on small price changes observed in retail settings. The 20-percent soda tax considered here is large in comparison to typical retail price variation. From appendix table 3, we can see that a 20-percent increase in the mean price of caloric sweetened beverages is larger than the observed range in our data.

When price increases or taxes are large, elasticities may underestimate actual consumer reactions. This may be particularly true if large taxes are fortified by complementary consumer education policies. For example, large State and Federal cigarette taxes (on average 85 percent of the average before-tax price or 46 percent of the average after-tax price (Campaign for Tobacco Free Kids, 2010)) combined with government and private tobacco control campaigns have been credited with the large reductions in U.S. cigarette use (Chaloupka, 2010).

Using the National Health Interview Survey, the CDC estimates that the share of adults who smoke fell from 42.4 percent to 20.6 percent between 1965 and 2008—a result that many would not have predicted given economists' shortrun estimates of inelastic cigarette demand (average estimate -0.48 (Gallet and List, 2003)). (See Chaloupka 2010; Engelhard et al., 2009 for reviews of the tobacco-tax literature.)

Table 3. Changes in daily beverage consumption

A tax-induced 20-percent increase in the price of caloric sweetened beverages could produce an overall reduction in calorie intake from beverages

Beverage categories	Adults	Changes in daily consumption Children		
	Ounces	Calories	Ounces	Calories
All beverages	-3.63	-36.9	-3.78	-42.7
Caloric sweetened beverages	-3.63	-38.8	-4.45	-48.8
Diet beverages	-0.11	0.0	-0.05	0.0
Skim milk	0.01	0.1	0.02	0.2
Low-fat milk	0.03	0.4	0.08	1.2
Whole milk	0.03	0.6	0.10	1.7
Juices	0.13	1.7	0.27	3.6
Coffee/tea	-0.58	-0.9	-0.13	-0.5
Bottled water	0.48	0.0	0.37	0.0

Source: ERS calculations based on 2003-06 National Health and Nutrition Examination Survey (NHANES) (8,460 adults and 7,365 children).

Calculating Changes in Calorie Consumption and Weight Status

The figure below represents a hypothetical individual's intake and the calculations used to derive changes in calorie intake and body weight. This method is carried out for all individuals in 2003-06 NHANES who drank caloric-sweetened beverages.

Those who did not drink caloric sweetened beverages were unaffected by the tax.

We need only to consider the elasticities presented in the first column of appendix table 4. These elasticities reflect the percentage change in purchases from each beverage category due to a 1-percent change in the price of caloric sweetened beverages (A). Under our scenario, the price of caloric sweetened beverages increases by 20 percent due to a tax and must be reflected in the percentage change in purchases (B). To translate changes in consumption from purchase decisions, we must assume a one-to-one translation—the percentage change in purchases is equivalent to the percentage change in consumption. Multiplying column B by each individual's calorie intake from each beverage category (C) yields that individual's change in daily calorie intake (D). Averaging these changes in calorie intake (D) over the entire population yields the average change in daily calorie intake found in table 3. Assuming that 1 pound of body weight has about 3,500 calories, we calculate each NHANES respondent's weight reduction over 1 year (E). Each individual's new, hypothetical weight can be used to recalculate overweight and obesity prevalence for the U.S. population.

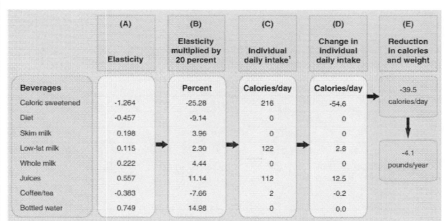

		(A)	(B)	(C)	(D)	(E)
		Elasticity	Elasticity multiplied by 20 percent	Individual daily intake[1]	Change in individual daily intake	Reduction in calories and weight
Beverages			Percent	Calories/day	Calories/day	-39.5 calories/day
Caloric sweetened		-1.264	-25.28	216	-54.6	
Diet		-0.457	-9.14	0	0	
Skim milk		0.198	3.96	0	0	
Low-fat milk		0.115	2.30	122	2.8	-4.1 pounds/year
Whole milk		0.222	4.44	0	0	
Juices		0.557	11.14	112	12.5	
Coffee/tea		-0.383	-7.66	2	-0.2	
Bottled water		0.749	14.98	0	0.0	

[1] Example individual: Adult male, 5 foot 10 inches, weighing 175 pounds would have a BMI of 25.1—overweight. The calorie contents represent the following: 12 ounces of cola, 8 ounces of fruit drink, 8 ounces of 2 percent milk, 8 ounces of orange juice, and 8 ounces of unsweetened brewed tea. After the tax, assuming elasticities and all else constant, the adult male would lose 4.1 pounds of body weight over 1 year, reducing his BMI to 24.5 —normal weight.

WHAT HAPPENS TO OVERWEIGHT AND OBESITY PREVALENCE?

NHANES respondents' body weight and height were measured during the survey. The body weight and height data were used to determine an individual's BMI, which is the basis for classifying weight status. For adults, *overweight* and *obesity* thresholds are a BMI score of 25 and 30, respectively. For children, the Centers for Disease Control and Prevention (CDC) child growth charts are used, and the 85th and 95th percentiles are the thresholds to classify children (ages 2-19) as *at risk for overweight* and *overweight*, respectively (Kuczmarski et al., 2002).

The dynamic relationship between calorie intake and body weight is quite complex. Weight loss is the result of an energy imbalance (excessive calorie expenditure over intake), and maintaining such an imbalance will lead to long-term changes in weight. When an individual loses weight, he/she will need fewer calories to maintain the lower body weight—given a fixed reduction in daily energy intake, an individual's weight will decrease but then saturate to a new steady state, which can take several years to achieve (Chow and Hall, 2008). One frequently used relationship in textbooks (e.g., Whitney et al., 2002) and scientific articles (e.g., Duffey et al., 2010) is that a pound of fat tissue has about 3,500 calories, which we use to predict the tax-induced weight loss and the resulting changes in the overweight and obesity prevalence.

Assuming that everything else remains equal (e.g., constant physical activity level and no shift to foods other than beverages), a reduction of 3,500 calories leads to a 1-pound loss in body weight (Whitney et al., 2002). Individuals' body weight reductions can be used to compare the associated before- and after-tax prevalence of overweight and obesity in the United States. We predict that the overweight prevalence among adults could decline from 66.9 to 62.4 percent, and the prevalence of obese adults could decline from 33.4 to 30.4 percent. For children, the at-risk-for-overweight prevalence could decline from 32.3 to 27.0 percent, and the prevalence of overweight children could decline from 16.6 to 13.7 percent.

These reductions in overweight and obesity prevalence are the result of two factors. First, a large group of adults and children are overweight or obese by only a few pounds. A small reduction in calorie intake could change the weight classification among these individuals. Second, many overweight adults and children consume large quantities of caloric sweetened beverages. Under our assumptions, individuals with a higher consumption of taxed beverages would be affected more by the tax than those who consume less. For example, the overweight adults who would shift to a healthy weight after the 20-percent tax consumed 496 calories a day from caloric sweetened beverages compared with 100 calories consumed by those who remain overweight under the tax. Obese adults who would become nonobese consumed 474 calories a day from caloric sweetened beverages compared with 127 calories consumed by those who remain obese.

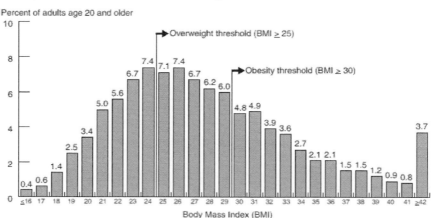

Source: ERS calculations based on 2003-06 National Health and Nutrition Examination Survey (NHANES) data.
Note: Each BMI value is inclusive (e.g., BMI of 25 includes those with a BMI of 25 to 25.9)

Figure 4. Share of adults at each BMI level.

In addition, many individuals are just a few pounds below the BMI cutoffs for overweight and obesity (fig. 4). Reduced consumption of caloric sweetened beverages triggered by the tax could prevent them from joining the ranks of the obese or overweight.

DISCUSSION

The use of economic incentives or disincentives to encourage healthful food choices has received heightened attention among policymakers in an effort to improve the American diet. The rich food-demand literature suggests that many foods are generally own-price inelastic—that is, the percentage change in consumption is smaller than the percentage change in price (Andreyeva et al., 2010). Under inelastic demand, price manipulations alone will not induce large consumer responses. This finding is echoed in analyses examining the effects of taxing salty snacks and fat in dairy products (Kuchler et al., 2004; Chouinard et al., 2007), as well as subsidizing fruit, vegetable, and dairy consumption (Lin et al., 2010). Our results in the present study suggest that the demand for caloric sweetened beverages is own-price elastic, suggesting consumers are relatively responsive to price changes—a 10-percent price increase is estimated to reduce purchases by 12.6 percent.

To promote healthier food choices, alternative strategies to taxing caloric sweetened beverages exist—subsidizing healthier beverage choices, restricting supply of unhealthy beverages, or improving informational campaigns. Many of these types of policies have been implemented for children in schools. For example, 31 States had policies limiting access to and/or setting nutrition standards for competitive foods in schools in 2009, including caloric sweetened beverages (Trust for America's Health, 2009). Likewise, the National School Lunch Program offers subsidized milk and requires milk as a menu component. Consequently, school meals are found to be calcium rich, compared with meals eaten by children elsewhere (Lin et al., 1999). If the objective is to reduce the obesity prevalence, however, it is important to note that some juices and reduced-fat milk contain more calories than sodas.

Children have also responded positively to lowering the price of healthy snacks and raising the price of less healthy snacks in school settings (French et al., 2001; Jeffrey et al., 1994). The same pricing strategy could be considered to encourage healthier beverage choices at school. It is important to point out, however, that results from in-school experiments may not apply to retail food markets because children have unique utility functions, partly due to their limited resources and the restricted variety of snacks available in schools.

Type of Tax Matters

Economists are often tasked with calculating consumers' responsiveness to price signals. For a consumer to respond to a tax, he or she must be aware of the tax-induced price change. In this analysis, we assumed that consumers would be cognizant of the 20-percent price increase in caloric sweetened beverages as a result of a tax. But would this be true in the marketplace?

A sales tax is applied as items are rung up at checkout and not displayed on the grocery store shelf. Consumers are often not aware of the tax burden from a particular item or may not consider a sales tax when making food purchase choices at grocery stores or restaurants (McLaughlin, 2009), possibly explaining previous findings that BMI was not associated with State-level taxes (e.g., Fletcher et al., 2009; Powell et al., 2009; Sturm et al., 2010; Fletcher et al., 2010). In addition, grocery purchases of beverages and other eligible foods within USDA's Supplemental Nutrition Assistance Program (SNAP, formerly known as the Food Stamp Program) are exempt from sales taxes (USDA/FNS, 2010). Thus, SNAP recipients would not be subject to the higher price in grocery stores that result from a sales tax.

Caloric sweetened beverages could also be taxed through an excise tax on drink manufacturers based on the quantity of the beverage produced or on the amount of sugar and syrups used in their products. If the tax is then passed on to retailers, who, in turn, incorporate it into a higher retail price, the price increase is displayed on the supermarket shelf or restaurant menu. An excise tax will be more likely to affect food choices, including grocery purchases for SNAP benefit recipients.

Reactions of Beverage Companies and Retailers Affect Impact of Tax

Manufacturers' and retailers' responses to taxes—both sales and excise taxes—affect the size of the tax-induced price increase paid by consumers. If the higher cost from an excise tax is not passed through to the consumer or partially absorbed by the manufacturer or retailer, the effect of the tax is dampened. For example, manufacturers could fully absorb an excise tax and not raise the prices of the taxed beverages, or they could raise prices by less than the full tax rate. If only a portion of the excise tax is passed on to the consumer, then an excise tax greater than 20 percent would be required to cause a 20-percent price increase. Similarly, retailers have freedom to set shelf prices; they could adjust prices to compensate for a tax.

The market structure of the beverage industry can also make it difficult to predict how manufacturers and suppliers of caloric sweetened beverages would change their competitive strategies, if at all, in reaction to a tax on their products. Beverage manufacturers could spread the cost of the excise tax across their products by raising prices of both taxed and nontaxed beverages, creating a situation where the relative price of caloric sweetened beverages versus alternative beverages would essentially remain unchanged. Under this scenario, consumers would be less likely to choose alternative beverages, again, dampening the effect of the tax. For the same reasons, it is also difficult to predict the influence that a tax on caloric sweetened beverages would have on the employment and local economy.

Using taxes or other disincentives to influence consumption is a complicated undertaking with many unknowns. Modeling consumers' responsiveness to higher prices resulting from a tax on caloric sweetened beverages is just one step in predicting the impact of the tax. Responsiveness at the individual or household level could vary across other elements, such as personal preference and income level. The ultimate outcome would depend on many factors, including the size of the tax, the type of tax, and the competitive strategies of beverage manufacturers and food retailers.

APPENDIX 1. STATE BEVERAGE TAXES

Appendix Table 1. State-level sales taxes of general food and sodas, effective January 2009

State	Food sales	Soda sales	Soda vending	State	Food sales	Soda sales	Soda vending
	Tax rate (percent)		----		*Tax rate (percent)*		
Alabama	4.0	4.0	4.0	Missouri	1.225	1.225	1.225
Alaska	0.0	0.0	0.0	Montana	0.0	0.0	0.0
Arizona	0.0	0.0	0.0	Nebraska	0.0	0.0	5.5
Arkansas	3.0	3.0	3.0	Nevada	0.0	0.0	0.0
California	0.0	6.25	6.25	New Hampshire	0.0	0.0	0.0
Colorado	0.0	0.0	0.0	New Jersey	0.0	7.0	7.0
Connecticut	0.0	6.0	6.0	New Mexico	0.0	0.0	5.0
Delaware	0.0	0.0	0.0	New York	0.0	4.0	4.0
District of				North Carolina	0.0	4.5	4.5
Columbia	0.0	0.0	5.75	North Dakota	0.0	5.0	5.0
Florida	0.0	6.0	6.0	Ohio	0.0	5.5	5.5
Georgia	0.0	0.0	4.0	Oklahoma	4.5	4.5	4.5
Hawaii*	4.0	4.0	4.0	Oregon	0.0	0.0	0.0
Idaho	6.0	6.0	6.0	Pennsylvania	0.0	6.0	6.0
Illinois	1.0	6.25	6.25	Rhode Island	0.0	7.0	7.0
Indiana	0.0	7.0	7.0	South Carolina	0.0	0.0	6.0
Iowa	0.0	6.0	6.0	South Dakota	4.0	4.0	4.0

Appendix Table 1. (Continued)

State	Food sales	Soda sales	Soda vending	State	Food sales	Soda sales	Soda vending
	Tax rate (percent)		----		*Tax rate (percent)*		
Kansas	5.3	5.3	5.3	Tennessee	5.5	5.5	5.5
Kentucky	0.0	6.0	6.0	Texas	0.0	6.25	6.25
Louisiana	0.0	0.0	0.0	Utah	1.75	1.75	1.75
Maine	0.0	5.0	5.0	Vermont	0.0	0.0	0.0
Maryland	0.0	6.0	6.0	Virginia	1.5	1.5	4.0
Massachusetts	0.0	0.0	0.0	Washington	0.0	6.5	6.5
Michigan	0.0	0.0	0.0	West Virginia	3.0	6.0	6.0
Minnesota	0.0	6.5	6.5	Wisconsin	0.0	5.0	5.0
Mississippi	7.0	7.0	8.0	Wyoming	0.0	0.0	4.0

* Hawaii does not levy a specific soda sales tax, but rather a general excise tax.
Source: Compiled from Bridging the Gap, 2010.

Appendix Table 2. State-level nonsales taxes placed on sodas, effective January 2009

State	Tax
Alabama	1. License tax placed on manufacturers of soda bottles based on bottling machine output—from $40 for machines with 16 bottles per minute of output to $500 for 150 bottles or more per minute. 2. Annual license fee placed on retailers ($2.50; waived if retailer also sales soda by means of a tap) and wholesalers ($50; waived if wholesaler has a bottling license) of soda bottles. 3. Annual license fee place on retailers of soda sold via a dispensing device or tap based on number of residents—$10 for less than 5,000; $15 for 5,000 to 15,000; $20 for 15,000 to 20,000; and $25 for over 25,000—in addition to an additional $2.50 annual tax.
Arizona	1. Privilege tax of $0.21 per gallon placed on manufacturers, distributors, wholesalers, or retailers of soda bottles; waived for retailers if purchased from a licensed manufacturer, distributor, or wholesaler. 2. Privilege tax of $2 per gallon placed on manufacturers, distributors, wholesalers, or retailers of syrup used in sodas; waived for retailers if purchased from a licensed manufacturer, distributor, or wholesaler. 3. Privilege tax of $0.21 per gallon of soft drinks made from a powder mix according to manufacturer's directions placed on manufacturers, distributors, wholesalers, or retailers; waived for retailers if mix is purchased from a licensed manufacturer, distributor, or wholesaler.
Rhode Island	1. Excise tax of $0.04 per case (24, 12 ounce cans) of sodas placed on manufacturers.
Tennessee	1. Privilege tax of 1.9 percent of gross receipts of sodas placed on manufacturers and retailers.

State	Tax	
Virginia	1.	Excise tax placed on distributors and wholesalers of sodas varying from $50 to $33,000 depending on gross receipts
Washington	1.	Excise tax of $1 per gallon of syrup placed on wholesalers and retailers of soda syrup, unless previously taxed.
West Virginia*	1.	Excise tax of $0.01 per half liter of soda placed on manufacturers, distributors, wholesalers, or retailers of soda.
	2.	Excise tax of $0.80 per gallon of soda syrup place on manufacturers, distributors, wholesalers, or retailers of soda syrup.
	3.	Excise tax of $0.84 per 4 liters of soda syrup place on manufacturers, distributors, wholesalers, or retailers of soda syrup.

*West Virginia has two provisions for an excise tax on syrups based on a gallon and 4 liters, although they are technically the same, because the statutes cannot be reconciled.

Source: Bridging the Gap, 2010.

APPENDIX 2. BEVERAGE DEMAND MODEL

In this study, we estimated a beverage demand system in which beverage categories are distinguished by calorie content. A complete food demand system was not estimated, but rather separability between beverages and other food items was assumed in food budgeting and a sub-system of the eight beverages was estimated (caloric-sweetened beverages, diet drinks, skim milk, low-fat milk, whole milk, juice, coffee/tea, and bottled water).

The Almost Ideal Demand System (AIDS, Deaton and Muellbauer, 1980) is used for the empirical estimation of a beverage demand system. The AIDS can be specified as:

$$w_i = \alpha_i + \sum_i \gamma_{ij} \ln p_j + \beta_i \ln(m/P^*) + e_i \qquad i = 1, \dots, n, \qquad (1)$$

where w_i is the beverage expenditure share for beverage i; p_j is the price for beverage j; m is the total expenditure for all beverages; α_i, γ_{ij}, and β_i are the parameters to be estimated; and e_i is the disturbance term. P is a price index defined by:

$$\ln P = \alpha_0 + \sum_i \alpha_i \ln p_i + 1/2 \sum_i \sum_j \gamma_{ij}^* \ln p_i \ln p_j \qquad (2)$$

and $\gamma_{ij} = (\gamma_{ij}^* + \gamma_{ij}^*)/2$. Equation 1 can be considered as the first-order approximation to the general unknown relation between w_i and $\ln m$, and the $\ln p$'s. Shift variables, such as the average U.S. monthly temperature and a time trend, are incorporated into the AIDS using a specification suggested by Alston et al. (2001). According to the Alston et al. specification, these demand shifters can be incorporated into equation 1 as

$$w_i = \alpha_i{}^* + \sum_i \gamma_{ij} \ln p_j + \beta_i \ln(m/\boldsymbol{P}^*) + e_i \qquad i = 1, \ldots, n, \qquad (3)$$

where $\alpha_i{}^* = \alpha_i + \varphi_{1i}$ (temperature) $+ \varphi_{2i}$ (time trend); $\ln\boldsymbol{P}^* = \alpha_0{}^* + \sum \alpha_i{}^* \ln p_i + 1/2 \sum_i\sum_j \gamma_{ij}{}^* \ln p_i \ln p_j$; and $\alpha_0{}^* = \alpha_0 + \upsilon_{1i}$ (temperature) $+ \upsilon_{2i}$ (time trend). Adding-up conditions are given by:

$$\sum_i \alpha_i = 1, \ \sum_i \beta_i = 0, \ \sum_i \gamma_{ij} = 0, \ \sum_i \varphi_{1i} = 0, \ \sum_i \varphi_{2i} = 0 \qquad (4)$$

Homogeneity and symmetry conditions require:

$$\sum_j \gamma_{ij} = 0 \text{ for all } i \text{ and } \gamma_{ij} = \gamma_{ji} \text{ for all } i, j \ (i \neq j) \qquad (5)$$

The price index P^* is scaled to unity at the sample means of prices and the constant term in equation 2 and α_0 was restricted to be zero (Moschini, 1998). Conditional expenditure (ε_i) and uncompensated price $_{(\varepsilon_{ij})}$ elasticity estimates at sample means can be calculated as:

$$\varepsilon_i = 1 + \beta_i/w_i \qquad (6)$$

and

$$\varepsilon_{ij} = (\gamma_{ij} - \beta_i (w_j - \beta_j \ln (m/P^*))/w_i - \delta_{ij} \qquad (7)$$

where δ_{ij} is the Kronnecker delta that is unity if $i = j$ and zero otherwise.

Variable definitions and summary statistics can be found in appendix table 3. The iterative seemingly-unrelated-regression technique (TSP, version 5.0) was used to estimate the model represented by equation 3 with homogeneity and symmetry conditions (equation 5) imposed. As the data add up by construction, the error covariance matrix was singular and an arbitrary equation was excluded (the model estimates are invariant to the equation deleted as shown by Barten 1969). The parameters of the excluded equation can be obtained from the adding-up conditions (equation 4) or by re-estimating the model, omitting a different equation.

Appendix Table 3. Variable definitions and summary statistics, 1998-2007

Variable	Definition	Mean	St. Dev.	Minimum	Maximum
p_1	Nominal price for caloric sweetened beverages, \$/gal	2.62	0.17	2.32	3.04
p_2	Nominal price for diet beverages, \$/gal	2.00	0.16	1.69	2.35
p_3	Nominal price for skim milk, \$/gal	2.80	0.26	2.46	3.72
p_4	Nominal price for low-fat milk, \$/gal	2.77	0.28	2.43	3.70
p_5	Nominal price for whole milk, \$/gal	2.98	0.31	2.61	3.96
p_6	Nominal price for juice, \$/gal	4.36	0.44	3.68	5.55
p_7	Nominal price for coffee/tea, \$/gal	4.03	0.33	3.17	4.76
p_8	Nominal price for bottled water, \$/gal	1.40	0.16	1.04	1.63
w_1	Beverage budget share for caloric sweetened beverages	0.34	0.03	0.28	0.40
w_2	Beverage budget share for diet beverages	0.16	0.01	0.14	0.20
w_3	Beverage budget share for skim milk	0.06	0.01	0.04	0.07
w_4	Beverage budget share for low-fat milk	0.14	0.01	0.12	0.16
w_5	Beverage budget share for whole milk	0.06	0.01	0.05	0.07
w_6	Beverage budget share for juice	0.16	0.01	0.13	0.19
w_7	Beverage budget share for coffee/tea	0.02	0.01	0.01	0.04
w_8	Beverage budget share for bottled water	0.06	0.02	0.03	0.11
φ_1	Average U.S. monthly temperature	54.37	14.93	28.68	77.26

Sources: Prices and budget shares are ERS calculations based on Nielsen Homescan (1998-2007). Temperature is measured in Fahrenheit (NOAA, 2009).
St. Dev.=Standard deviation. \$/gal=Dollars per gallon.

By estimating the conditional AIDS for beverages shown by equation 3, first-order autocorrelation was found to exist, which required estimating an additional parameter ρ (Berndt and Savin, 1975). In this model, each equation included only the lagged error for that equation, but to satisfy adding up, the seven autocorrelation parameters were constrained to be equal. The 120-month time-series data were fitted by the nonlinear AIDS model, and demand price elasticities were derived using equations 6 and 7. For brevity, the parameter estimates are not reported, and the demand elasticities are reported in appendix table 4. The estimated autocorrelation coefficient, ρ, had a value of 0.71 with a likelihood ratio test statistic of 267.78.

Appendix Table 4. U.S. beverage demand elasticities, 1998-2007

| Beverage | Uncompensated price elasticities | | | | | | | | Expenditure elasticities |
	εi1	εi2	εi3	εi4	εi5	εi6	εi7	εi8	εi
Caloric sweetened beverages	-1.264***	-0.192***	0.023	0.015	0.028	0.233***	-0.027	0.131***	1.054***
	(0.089)	(0.048)	(0.016)	(0.036)	(0.023)	(0.045)	(0.019)	(0.035)	(0.041)
Diet beverages	-0.457***	-0.753***	0.042	0.064	-0.165***	0.096	-0.020	-0.044	1.238***
	(0.103)	(0.106)	(0.026)	(0.052)	(0.042)	(0.071)	(0.031)	(0.057)	(0.051)
Skim milk	0.198**	0.184**	-0.830***	-0.015	0.371***	-0.432***	-0.061*	-0.296***	0.880***
	(0.097)	(0.076)	(0.166)	(0.190)	(0.149)	(0.084)	(0.033)	(0.058)	(0.046)
Low-fat milk	0.115	0.144**	-0.003	-0.707***	0.055	-0.277***	0.037	-0.187***	0.822***
	(0.088)	(0.061)	(0.076)	(0.138)	(0.105)	(0.064)	(0.025)	(0.045)	(0.047)
Whole milk	0.222*	-0.371***	0.332***	0.119	-1.122***	-0.253**	-0.049	0.281***	0.841***
	(0.126)	(0.108)	(0.133)	(0.231)	(0.243)	(0.113)	(0.044)	(0.077)	(0.059)
Juices	0.557***	0.159**	-0.151***	-0.248***	-0.102**	-1.012***	0.006	-0.087*	0.878***
	(0.095)	(0.071)	(0.029)	(0.055)	(0.044)	(0.090)	(0.028)	(0.051)	(0.048)
Coffee/tea	-0.383	-0.103	-0.149**	0.179	-0.139	0.011	-0.451***	-0.018	1.053***
	(0.264)	(0.207)	(0.075)	(0.141)	(0.115)	(0.188)	(0.121)	(0.155)	(0.125)
Bottled water	0.749***	-0.088	-0.284***	-0.460***	0.282***	-0.255*	-0.007	-0.969***	1.032***
	(0.196)	(0.153)	(0.053)	(0.102)	(0.080)	(0.135)	(0.062)	(0.157)	(0.100)

Source: ERS calculations based on Nielsen Homescan data, 1998-2007.

Notes: ***, **, and * indicate a level of significance of 1, 5, and 10 percent, respectively. Standard errors are in parentheses. Highlighted numbers indicate uncompensated own-price elasticities; all other uncompensated elasticities are cross-price estimates.

REFERENCES

Alston J.M., J.A. Chalfant, and N.E. Piggott. "Incorporating demand shifters in the Almost Ideal demand system," *Economic Letters* 70(1): pp. 73-8, 2001.

Andreyeva T., M.W. Long, and K.D. Brownell. "The impact of food prices on consumption: A systematic review of research on price elasticity of demand for food," *American Journal of Public Health* 100(2): pp. 216-22, 2009.

Barten A.P. "Maximum likelihood estimation of a complete system of demand equations," *European Economic Review* 1(1): pp. 7-73, 1969.

Bergtold J., E. Akobundu, and E.B. Peterson. "The FAST method: Estimating unconditional demand elasticities for processed foods in the presence of fixed effects," *Journal of Agricultural and Resource Economics* 29(2): pp. 276-95, 2004.

Berndt, E.R., and N.E. Savin. "Estimation and hypothesis testing in singular equation systems with autoregressive disturbances," *Econometrica* 43(5-6): pp. 937-56, 1975.

Bridging the Gap. *State Snack and Soda Tax Data,* Bridging the Gap Program, University of Illinois at Chicago, 2010, http://www. impacteen.org/obesitystatedata.htm.

Brownell, K.D., T. Farley, W.C. Willett, B.M. Popkin, F.J. Chaloupka, J.W. Thompson, and D.S. Ludwig. "The public health and economic benefits of taxing sugar-sweetened beverages," *New England Journal of Medicine* 361(16): pp. 1599-1605, 2009.

Brownell, K.D., and T.R. Frieden. "Ounces of prevention—the public policy case for taxes on sugared beverages," *New England Journal of Medicine* 360(18): pp. 1805-08, 2009.

Centers for Disease Control and Prevention. *Obesity and overweight,* 2010, http://www.cdc.gov/obesity/index.html.

Centers for Disease Control and Prevention, National Center for Health Statistics. *National Health and Nutrition Examination Survey, 2003–2004 and 2005–2006,* Atlanta, GA, 2009, http://www.cdc.gov/nchs/nhanes.htm.

Chaloupka, F. "Tobacco Control Lessons Learned: The Impact of State and Local Policies." Chicago, IL: ImpactTeen, Research paper series, No. 38, 2010.

Chaloupka, F.J., L.M. Powell, and J.F. Chriqui. *Sugar-Sweetened Beverage Taxes and Public Health,* research brief, Robert Wood Johnson Foundation and School of Public Health, University of Minnesota, July 2009.

Chouinard H., D. Davis, J. Lafrance, and J. Perloff. "Fat taxes: Big money for small change," *Forum for Health Economics and Policy* 10(2), Article 2, 2007.

Deaton, A.S., and J.N. Muellbauer. "An almost ideal demand system," *American Economic Review* 70(3): pp. 312–26, 1980.

Dennis, E.A., K.D. Flack, and B.M. Davy. "Beverage consumption and adult weight management: A review," *Eating Behaviors* 10(4): pp. 237-46, 2009.

Dhar, T., J. Chavas, and R. Cotterill. *An Economic Analysis of Product Differentiation Under Latent Separability,* paper prepared for the Annual Meeting of the American Association of Agricultural Economics, Montreal, Canada, July 27-30, 2003.

Dietz, W. "Sugar-sweetened beverages, milk intake, and obesity in children and adolescents," *Journal of Pediatrics* 148(2): pp. 152-54, 2006.

DiMeglio, D.P., and R. Mattes. "Liquid versus solid carbohydrate: Effects on food intake and body weight," *International Journal of Obesity and Related Metabolic Disorders* 24(6): pp. 794-800, 2000.

Duffey, K.J., and B.M. Popkin. "Shifts in patterns and consumption of beverages between 1965 and 2002," *Obesity* 15(11): pp. 2739-47, 2007.

Duffey, K.J., Penny Gordon-Larsen, James M. Shikany, David Guilkey, David R. Jacobs Jr., and Barry M. Popkin. "Food price and diet and heath outcomes: 20 years of the CARDIA study," *Archives of Internal Medicine* 170(5): pp. 420-26, 2010.

Engelhard, C.L., A, Garson, and S Dorn. *Reducing Obesity: Policy Strategies from the Tobacco Wars.* Washington D.C.: Urban Institute, 2009.

Finkelstein, E.A., J.G. Trogdon, J.W. Cohen, and W. Dietz. "Annual medical spending attributable to obesity: Payer- and service-specific estimates," *Health Affairs* 28(5): pp. 822-31, 2009.

Fletcher, J.M., D. Frisvold, and N. Tefft. "Can soft drink taxes reduce population weight?" *Contemporary Economic Policy* 28(1): pp. 23-35, 2010.

Fletcher, J.M., D. Frisvold, and N. Tefft. "Taxing soft drinks and restricting access to vending machines to curb child obesity," *Health Affairs* 29(5): doi: 10.1377/hlthaff.2009.0725, 2010.

French S., R. Jeffery, M Story., K. Breitlow, J. Baxter, P. Hannan, and M. Snyder. Pricing and promotion effects on low-fat vending snack purchases: The CHIPS study. *American Journal of Public Health* 91, 112-117, 2001.

Gallet, CA, and JA. List. "Cigarette demand: a meta-analysis of elasticities." *Health Economics* 12(10):821-835, 2003.

Guenther, P.M., J. Reedy, S.M. Krebs-Smith, B.B. Reeve, and P.P. Basiotis. *Development and Evaluation of the Healthy Eating Index– 2005: Technical Report*, U.S. Department of Agriculture, Center for Nutrition Policy and Promotion, 2007, http://www.cnpp.usda.gov/ Healthy EatingIndex.htm.

Institute of Medicine. *Dietary Reference Intakes for Energy, Carbohydrate, Fiber, Fat, Fatty Acids, Cholesterol, Protein, and Amino Acids*, Washington, DC: National Academy of Sciences, 2002.

Institute of Medicine, Committee on Childhood Obesity Prevention Actions for Local Governments. *Location government actions to prevent childhood obesity*, (eds., Lynn Parker, Annina Catherine Burns, and Eduardo Sanchez), Washington, DC: National Academy of Sciences, 2009.

Jacobson, M.F., and K.D. Brownell. "Small taxes on soft drinks and snack foods to promote health," *American Journal of Public Health* 90(6): pp. 854–57, 2000.

Jeffrey R., S. French, C. Raether, and J. Baxter. "An environmental intervention to increase fruit and salad purchases in a cafeteria." *Preventive Medicine* 23, 788-792, 1994.

Kinnucan, H.W., Y. Miao, J. Xiao, and H.M. Kaiser. "Effects of advertising on U.S. non-alcoholic beverage demand: Evidence from a two-stage Rotterdam model," *Advances in Applied Microeconomics* (eds., M.R. Baye and J.P. Nelson), Amsterdam: Elsevier Science, 2001.

Kuczmarski, R.J., C.L. Ogden, S.S. Guo, L.M. Grummer-Strawn, K.M. Flegal, Z. Mei, R. Wei, L.R. Curtin, A.F. Roche, and C.L. Johnson. "2000 CDC Growth Charts for the United States: methods and development," *Vital and Health Statistics* 246(May): pp. 1-190, 2002.

Kuchler F., A. Tegene, and J. Harris. "Taxing snack foods: Manipulating diet quality or financing information programs?" *Review of Agricultural Economics* 27, 4-20, 2004.

Lin B., E. Frazao, and J. Guthrie. *Away-From-Home Foods Increasingly Important to Quality of American Diet.* Agriculture Information Bulletin No. 749, Economic Research Service, U.S. Department of Agriculture, 22p, 1999.

Lin B., S. Yen, D. Dong, and D. Smallwood. Economic incentives for dietary improvement among food stamp recipients. *Contemporary Economic Policy* (early view available, DOI: 10.1111/j.1465-7287.2009.00193.x), 2010.

Ludwig, D.S., K.E. Peterson, and S.L. Gortmaker. "Relation between consumption of sugar-sweetened drinks and childhood obesity: A prospective, observational analysis," *Lancet* 357(9255): pp. 505-8, 2001.

Lyon, H.L., and J.L. Simon. "Price elasticity of demand for cigarettes in the United States," *American Journal of Agricultural Economics* 50(4): pp. 888-95, 1968.

Malik, V.S., M.B. Schulze, and F.B. Hu. "Intake of sugar-sweetened beverages and weight gain: A systematic review," *American Journal of Clinical Nutrition* 84(2): pp. 274–88, 2006.

Mattes, R. "Dietary compensation by humans for supplemental energy provided as ethanol or carbohydrate in fluids," *Physiology and Behavior* 59(1): pp. 179-87, 1996.

Mattes, R. "Fluid calories and energy balance: The good, the bad, and the uncertain," *Physiology and Behavior* 89(1): pp. 66-70, 2006.

McLaughlin, I. Public Health Law and Policy, personal communications, November 13, 2009.

Moschini, G. "The semiflexible almost ideal demand system," *European Economic Review* 42(2): pp. 349-64, 1998.

National Oceanic Atmospheric Administration. *Contiguous United States climate summary*, 2009, http://www.ncdc.noaa.gov/oa/climate/research/cag3/na.html.

Nielsen Homescan. *Consumer Panel Solutions*, 2007, www.acnielsen.com/products/reports/homescan.

Peterson, D.E., S.L. Zeger, P.L. Remington, and H.A. Anderson. "The effect of state cigarette tax increases on cigarette sales, 1955 to 1988," *American Journal of Public Health* 82(1): pp. 94-6, 1992.

Piernas, C., and B.M. Popkin. "Snacking increased among United States adults between 1977 and 2006," *Journal of Nutrition* doi: 10.3945/jn.109.112763, 2009.

Powell, L.M., and F.J. Chaloupka. "Food prices and obesity: Evidence and policy implications for taxes and subsidies," *Milbank Quarterly* 87(1): pp. 229-57, 2009.

Powell, L.M., J. Chriqui, and F.J. Chaloupka. "Associations between state-level soda taxes and adolescent body mass index," *Journal of Adolescent Health* 45(3): pp. 57-63, 2009.

Rudd Center for Food Policy and Obesity. *Revenue calculator for soft drink taxes*, 2010, http://www.yaleruddcenter.org/sodatax.aspx.

Stull, A.J., J.W. Apolzan, A.E. Thalacker-Mercer, H.B. Iglay, and W.W. Campbell. "Liquid and solid meal replacement products differentially affect postprandial appetite and food intake in older adults," *Journal of the American Dietetic Association* 108(7): pp. 1226-30, 2008.

Sturm, R., L.M. Powell, J.F. Chriqui, and F.J. Chaloupka. "Soda taxes, soft drink consumption, and children's body mass index," *Health Affairs* 29(5) doi: 10.1377/hlthaff.2009.0725, 2010.

Trust for America's Health. Supplement to "F as in Fat: How Obesity Policies Are Failing in America, 2009": Obesity-Related Legislation Action in States, Update. http://healthyamericans.org/reports/obesity2009/ StateSupplement2009.pdf, 2009

Tsai, A.G., D.F. Williamson, and H.A. Glick. "Direct Medical Cost of Overweight and Obesity in the USA: A Quantitative Systematic Review," *Obesity Review* doi:10.i111/j.1467-789x.2009.00708.x.

TSP version 5.0. TSP International, Palo Alto, California, 2005.

U.S. Department of Agriculture. *Dietary Guidelines for Americans 2005.*

U.S. Department of Agriculture, Agricultural Research Service. *Nutrient Data Laboratory*, http://www.ars.usda.gov/main/site_main. htm?modecode=12-35-45-00.

U.S. Department of Agriculture, Economic Research Service. *Nutrient Availability Data Set*, http://www.ers.usda.gov/data/FoodConsumption/ NutrientAvailIndex.htm.

U.S. Department of Agriculture, Food and Nutrition Service. *Food Assistance Programs*, http://www.fns.usda.gov/fns/.

Vartanian, L.R., M.B. Schwartz, and K.D. Brownell. "Effects of soft drink consumption on nutrition and health: A systematic review and meta-analysis," *American Journal of Public Health* 97(4): pp. 667–75, 2007.

Wang, Y., M.A. Beydoun, L. Liang, B. Caballero, and S.K. Kumanyika. "Will all Americans become overweight or obese? Estimating the progression and cost the U.S. obesity epidemic," *Obesity* 16(10): pp. 2323-30, 2008.

White House Task Force on Childhood Obesity: Report to the President. "Solving the Problem of Childhood Obesity within a Generation." Washington, DC. May 2010. http://www.letsmove.gov/tfco_fullreport_may2010.pdf

Whitney, E.N., C.B. Cataldo, and S.R. Rolfes. *Understanding Normal and Clinical Nutrition,* sixth edition, Wadsworth/Thomson Learning, Belmont, California, 2002.

Yen, S.T., B.H. Lin, D.M. Smallwood, and M. Andrews. "Demand for nonalcoholic beverages: The case of low-income households," *Agribusiness* 20(3): pp. 309-21, 2004.

Zheng, Y., and H.M. Kaiser. "Advertising and U.S. nonalcoholic beverage demand," *Agricultural and Resource Economics Review* 31(2): pp. 147-59, 2008.

End Notes

[1] Body Mass Index (BMI) is a measure of weight adjusted for height calculated as an individual's weight in kilograms divided by the square of his or her height in meters.

[2] The -0.8 estimate is based on 14 studies with categories that included soft drinks, carbonated soft drinks, juice and soft drinks, soda, soda and fruit ades, nonalcoholic beverages, other beverages, or simply beverages. The -1.0 estimate is based on seven studies with categories that included soft drinks, carbonated soft drinks, soda or fruit ades, or soda. The range for all 14 studies was 0.13-3.18.

[3] Using the own- and cross-price elasticities and corresponding standard errors reported in appendix table 4, a 95-percent confidence interval was constructed: Net decline of [28.2 − 45.3] calories/day for adults, and [29.8 − 55.3] calories/day for children.

INDEX

D

E